LEVEL
5

motivation
MATH

student edition

D1091478

Critical Thinking for Life!™
Mentoring Minds

Publisher
Michael L. Lujan, M.Ed.

Editorial Director
Teresa Sherman, B.S.E.

Production Coordinator
Kim Barnes, B.B.A.

Digital Production Artists
Sarah Poff, B.S.
Judy Bankhead, M.F.A.
Tammy McDaniel
Gabe Urbina, A.A.S.

Illustrators
Sarah DuPree, B.F.A.
Gabe Urbina, A.A.S.

Content Development Team
Michael L. Lujan, M.Ed.
Teresa Sherman, B.S.E.
Marian Rainwater, M.Ed.
Karen White, M.Ed.
Stephanie Christian, M.Ed.
Amanda Byers, B.S.
Rebecca Clements, B.S.
Paula Jones, M.S.
R. Faith Morrow, M.S.

Content Editorial Team
Allison Wiley, B.S.E.
Marian Rainwater, M.Ed.
Karen White, M.Ed.
Nancy Roseman, B.S.E.
Karen Reeves, M.Ed.
Stephanie Christian, M.Ed.
Chasity Wisenbaker
Jennifer Mallios, B.A.

Critical Thinking for Life!™
Mentoring Minds

P.O. BOX 8843 • Tyler, TX 75711

800-585-5258 • FAX: 800-838-8186
For other great products from Mentoring Minds,
please visit our website at:
MentoringMinds.com

ISBN: 978-1-935123-72-9

TABLE OF CONTENTS

Dear Student,

We are Motivation Mike and Molly, and we think you are important. We want you to enjoy learning about math. Pay attention to your teachers and do your best each day. You will learn many new and interesting things to help you become successful in school and in life. Here are some tips to help you be the best possible student.

You Can Do It!

Your friends,
Motivation Mike and Molly

- Listen to your parents.
- Follow school rules.
- Listen to your teacher.
- Ask your teacher questions if you do not understand.
- Apply what you learn to your everyday life.
- Find friends who like school, and study with your friends.
- Get enough sleep each night.
- Eat proper meals, drink plenty of water, and exercise.
- Be positive.
- Never give up.

1. What is the value of this expression?

$$[(4 + 3) \times (8 - 2)] \div 2$$

Answer: _____

2. Sam and Sara discussed their grades on a math quiz. Sara showed Sam one of her incorrect problems.

Line 1: $\{80 + [2 \times (3\frac{1}{2} + 1\frac{1}{2})]\} \div 10$

Line 2: $\{80 + [2 \times 5]\} \div 10$

Line 3: $\{82 \times 5\} \div 10$

Line 4: $410 \div 10$

Line 5: 41

On which line did Sara make her first mistake? Show the correct steps to solve the problem.

Answer: _____

_____

_____

_____

3. Carina needs to simplify this expression.

$$2 \times 3 + [5 \times (14 - 6)]$$

What is the second step Carina should complete?

Answer: _____

4. Place grouping symbols in this numerical expression so that the solution is 11. Then show the steps to prove your answer is correct.

$$3 + 4 \times 2.5 - 0.5$$

Answer: _____

_____

_____

_____

5. Four students in Mrs. Gandy's class wrote the expressions shown on the chart.

Student	Expression
Amy	$2 \times (3 + 4 + 5) \div (6 + 2)$
Barney	$(4 + 3 + 2 + 1) \times 5$
Chloe	$2 \times [(3 + 7) \div 5] + 6$
Dexter	$3 \times [5 \times (4 + 2)]$

Write the names of the students so that the values of their expressions are in order from least to greatest.

_____

_____

_____

_____

Words for the Wise

braces	evaluate	numerical expressions
brackets	grouping symbols	parentheses

You shine!

partner practice

1. Hein places parentheses in the following expression:

$$9 \times 8.2 - 5 + 6.8 \div 2$$

Which of Hein's expressions would have the greatest value?

Ⓐ $[(9 \times 8.2) - 5] + (6.8 \div 2)$

Ⓑ $[9 \times (8.2 - 5)] + (6.8 \div 2)$

Ⓒ $(9 \times 8.2) - [(5 + 6.8) \div 2]$

Ⓓ $\{9 \times [(8.2 - 5 + 6.8)]\} \div 2$

2. Using the steps shown, Amelia incorrectly simplified this expression.

$$\{[5 + (24 \div 4)] - 4\} \times 2$$

Step 1: $\{[5 + 6] - 4\} \times 2$

Step 2: $\{11 - 4\} \times 2$

Step 3: $11 - 8$

Step 4: 3

Which step contains Amelia's first error?

Ⓐ Step 1

Ⓑ Step 2

Ⓒ Step 3

Ⓓ Step 4

3. Lei needs to simplify this expression.

$$18 \div 9 \times [(12 - 2) + 4]$$

Which operation will be performed last?

Ⓐ Add

Ⓑ Subtract

Ⓒ Multiply

Ⓓ Divide

4. Simplify this expression.

$$[(9 - 2) \times (2 + 1)] \div (\tfrac{1}{4} + \tfrac{3}{4})$$

What is the value of the simplified expression?

Ⓐ 3

Ⓑ 4

Ⓒ 16

Ⓓ 21

5. Corvian's teacher challenged the class to use grouping symbols to create an expression equal to 1. Which of the following expressions has a value of 1?

Ⓐ $\{(7 + 4) + [2 \times (9 - 4)]\} \div 7$

Ⓑ $\frac{1}{2} \times (\frac{2}{3} + \frac{4}{3})$

Ⓒ $[2 \times (1 + 3) + 1] - 7 + 1$

Ⓓ $7 + (1 \times \frac{1}{2}) - 3$

         Level 5

1. Xavier's teacher wrote this numerical expression.

$$200 - 50 - 4 \times 3 + 5$$

The four members of Xavier's group competed to see who could place grouping symbols in the expression to give the greatest solution. Their expressions are shown in this chart.

Student	Expression
Willy	$200 - \{[(50 - 4) \times 3] + 5\}$
Xavier	$200 - [50 - (4 \times 3 + 5)]$
Yolanda	$200 - 50 - [4 \times (3 + 5)]$
Zeva	$\{[200 - (50 - 4)] \times 3\} + 5$

Which list shows the students' names in order from the expression with the greatest value to the expression with the least value?

Ⓐ Zeva, Willy, Xavier, Yolanda

Ⓑ Zeva, Xavier, Yolanda, Willy

Ⓒ Xavier, Zeva, Willy, Yolanda

Ⓓ Zeva, Xavier, Willy, Yolanda

2. Reginald needs to create expressions equal to 4. He records some ideas, as shown here. Which of Reginald's expressions does **not** have a solution of 4?

Ⓐ $4 + [(4 \times 4) \div 4] - 4$

Ⓑ $(4 \times 4) - (4 \div 4) + 4$

Ⓒ $[(4 \div 4) \times (4 - 4)] + 4$

Ⓓ $4 + \{[(4 - 4) \times 4] \div 4\}$

3. Julia is simplifying this expression.

$$16 - \{8 \times [(3 + 6) \div 9]\}$$

These are the steps she has completed:

Step 1: $3 + 6 = 9$

Step 2: $9 \div 9 = 1$

Which of these should be Julia's next step?

Ⓐ $16 - 8 = 8$

Ⓑ $8 \times 9 = 72$

Ⓒ $16 - 9 = 7$

Ⓓ $8 \times 1 = 8$

4. What is the value of this expression?

$$4 \times [5 - (0.2 \times 3)] + 6$$

Ⓐ 10.0

Ⓑ 17.6

Ⓒ 23.6

Ⓓ 25.4

5. Which of the following does **not** have the same value as this expression?

$$[(180 \div 6) - 2] + (6 \times 2)$$

Ⓐ $(180 \div 6) - 2 + (6 \times 2)$

Ⓑ $(180 \div 6 - 2) + (6 \times 2)$

Ⓒ $180 \div 6 - 2 + (6 \times 2)$

Ⓓ $(180 \div 6) - (2 + 6 \times 2)$

★ assessment

1. Four students in a math competition placed grouping symbols in this expression.

$$3 \times 3.6 + 3 \times 5$$

Their results are shown on the chart.

Student	Expression
Abigail	$(3 \times 3.6) + (3 \times 5)$
Brenelsa	$3 \times (3.6 + 3) \times 5$
Cindy	$[(3 \times 3.6) + 3] \times 5$
Damarcus	$3 \times [3.6 + (3 \times 5)]$

Which list shows the students' names in order from the expression with the least value to the expression with the greatest value?

Ⓐ Abigail, Cindy, Damarcus, Brenelsa

Ⓑ Brenelsa, Cindy, Damarcus, Abigail

Ⓒ Damarcus, Abigail, Brenelsa, Cindy

Ⓓ Abigail, Damarcus, Cindy, Brenelsa

2. Adam solved this expression.

$$(12 \times 6) + 24 - (12 \div 4) - 2$$

Which expression has the same solution as the one Adam solved?

Ⓐ $12 \times (6 + 24) - [12 \div (4 - 2)]$

Ⓑ $[(12 \times 6) + 24] - [(12 \div 4) - 2]$

Ⓒ $[(12 \times 6) + 24] - (12 \div 4) - 2$

Ⓓ $(12 \times 6) + [(24 - 12) \div (4 - 2)]$

3. What is the value of this expression?

$$[78 \times (\tfrac{1}{4} + \tfrac{1}{4}) \div 3] \times 13$$

Ⓐ 169

Ⓑ $84\tfrac{1}{2}$

Ⓒ 13

Ⓓ 2

4. Using these steps, Uriel incorrectly simplified the expression and found an answer of 65.

$$\{90 \div [3 \times (1\tfrac{1}{2} + 1\tfrac{1}{2})]\} + 50$$

Step 1: $\{90 \div [3 \times 3]\} + 50$

Step 2: $\{90 \div 6\} + 50$

Step 3: $15 + 50$

Step 4: 65

Which step contains Uriel's first mistake? _____

Show the steps to solve Uriel's problem correctly. _____

 Level 5

Analysis/Analyze

1. James and John each wrote a numerical expression.

James: $18 \div 6 - 3$

John: $18 \div (6 - 3)$

Each boy believes his expression has the greater value. Who is right?   **Answer:** _____
Justify your answer.

_____

_____

_____

_____

Synthesis/Create

2. Create an expression with the greatest possible value by placing one or more sets of grouping symbols in this expression. You may use parentheses, brackets, braces, or any combination of symbols.

$$2 \times 5 + 3 + 6 \times 8 - 1$$

Answer: _____

Journal: Analysis/Analyze

In mathematics, parentheses are used as grouping symbols. How are parentheses used in language arts?

_____

_____

_____

Parenthetical Possibilities

Play *Parenthetical Possibilities* with a partner. Each player needs a game sheet, scratch paper, and a pencil. Each pair needs a number cube and a paper clip to use with a pencil on the spinner. One player rolls the number cube while the other player spins the spinner. The students select the expression below that corresponds to the number rolled and place grouping symbols (parentheses, brackets, and/or braces) in the expression to find a large or small answer, as indicated by the spinner. The player who finds the larger/smaller answer (as indicated by the spin) receives 1 point. Play continues until all expressions are used. If the number rolled matches an expression that has already been used, the player rolls again. If both answers are the same, each player scores 1 point. The winner is the player with the most points at the end of the game.

Expressions

1. $2 \times 5 + 8 - 4 \div 2$

2. $6 + 9 \times 6 \div 2 - 1$

3. $12 \div 2 + 4 \times 5 + 3$

4. $4 \times 4 - 3 + 6 \times 5$

5. $12 + 12 \div 3 \times 2 + 4$

6. $32 \div 4 + 4 \times 4 - 2$

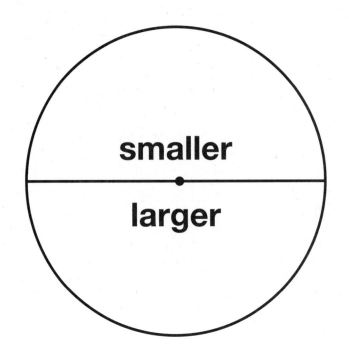

smaller

larger

Parent Activities

1. Using grocery store ads, write a list of items with the dollar amount and quantity of each item needed. Ask your child to write an expression showing how much money will be spent for the items on the list. Use parentheses to show when more than one of an item is being purchased. Your child might write an expression such as, $3.39 + (2 \times \$1.79) + (10 \times \$0.59)$. Help your child evaluate the expression to find the total amount of money that will be spent.

2. Using an old deck of cards, write a parenthesis on each Jack, an addition sign on each Queen, a subtraction sign on each King, a multiplication sign on each Ace, and a division sign on each Joker. Shuffle the deck and deal 7 cards to each player. Arrange the cards face up on the table to make equations. Give a point to the player who creates the equation with the greatest value.

1. Mrs. Bilby asked four students in her class to write an expression for this statement:

"Triple 8 and then subtract the sum of 2 and 8."

This table shows the students' expressions.

Student	Expression
Allison	(8 + 3) − (2 + 8)
Bert	(3 × 8) − (2 × 8)
Caroline	(3 × 8) − (2 + 8)
David	(2 + 8) − (8 + 8 × 8)

Which of the four students wrote a correct expression?

Answer: _____

2. Aaron and Ike wrote expressions to show how many baseball cards they each had left after a baseball card trading show.

Aaron's expression: $200 \div 2$

Ike's expression: $\frac{1}{4} \times (200 \div 2)$

Explain how the value of Aaron's expression compares to the value of Ike's expression.

_____

_____

_____

_____

3. Salima and Marco wrote these expressions.

Salima: $6 - 4$

Marco: $10 \times (6 - 4)$

Write a statement that correctly describes the relationship between the two expressions.

_____

_____

_____

4. Jameia's teacher wrote these words on the board.

"eight less than the product of one hundred three and forty-seven"

Write an expression to represent the words Jameia's teacher wrote.

Answer: _____

5. On their way to Camp Deer Run, Priscilla's family drove 135 miles and stopped for gasoline. Then they drove 40 more miles to the camp. Clifton's family also drove to Camp Deer Run, but they drove half as far as Priscilla's family. Write a numerical expression to represent the distance Clifton's family drove.

Answer: _____

_____

Words for the Wise

difference	parentheses	
double	product	sum
expression	quotient	triple

This is familiar territory!

partner practice

1. Mrs. Wallace wrote this statement.

   "Double three, then add ten to that product."

   Which expression **best** represents the statement Mrs. Wallace wrote?

   Ⓐ $10 + (2 \times 3)$

   Ⓑ $(10 + 3) \times 2$

   Ⓒ $10 + (3 \times 3)$

   Ⓓ $10 \times (2 \times 3)$

2. Shari and Ada each wrote and solved an expression. Shari found the difference between 354 and 187. Ada solved the expression $0.1 \times (354 - 187)$. Which statement correctly describes the relationship between these two expressions?

   Ⓐ The value of Shari's expression is one-tenth of the value of Ada's expression.

   Ⓑ The value of Shari's expression is 10 times greater than the value of Ada's expression.

   Ⓒ The value of Ada's expression is 10 times greater than the value of Shari's expression.

   Ⓓ Both Shari's and Ada's expressions have the same value.

3. Howard earns $5 per hour mowing grass. Yesterday he worked 6 hours. Then Howard gave his dad $4 to pay back a loan. Which expression represents the amount of money Howard had left after he paid his dad?

   Ⓐ $(5 \times 4) + 6$

   Ⓑ $(6 \times 5) - 4$

   Ⓒ $6 \times (5 - 4)$

   Ⓓ $(6 \times 5) \div 4$

4. At a basketball game, Ginger sold 46 sodas for $2 each. She wrote this expression to show her goal for soda sales at the next basketball game.

   $$3 \times (46 \times 2)$$

   Which statement **best** represents Ginger's goal for soda sales at the next basketball game?

   Ⓐ Ginger wants to sell sodas for $3 at the next basketball game.

   Ⓑ Ginger wants to sell one-third as many sodas at the next basketball game.

   Ⓒ Ginger wants to sell twice as many sodas at the next basketball game.

   Ⓓ Ginger wants to sell three times as many sodas at the next basketball game.

5. Compare these expressions.

   Expression 1: $678 - 217$

   Expression 2: $(678 - 217) \div 2$

   Expression 3: $10 \times (678 - 217)$

   Which statement is **not** true?

   Ⓐ The value of Expression 2 is the least of the three expressions.

   Ⓑ The value of Expression 3 is ten times as much as the value of Expression 1.

   Ⓒ The value of Expression 3 is ten times as much as the value of Expression 2.

   Ⓓ The value of Expression 2 is half as much as the value of Expression 1.

1. Misty read this phrase.

   "6 less than the product of 5 and 7"

   Which expression **best** represents the statement that Misty read?

   Ⓐ $6 - (5 \times 7)$

   Ⓑ $(5 \times 7) - 6$

   Ⓒ $(6 - 5) \times 7$

   Ⓓ $(6 \times 5) - 7$

2. Liz and 3 friends ate at the Snack Shack. They each ordered a drink for $2 and shared an order of chili-cheese fries for $7. Which expression can be used to calculate the total amount, in dollars, Liz and her friends paid?

   Ⓐ $(3 \times 2) + 7$

   Ⓑ $(4 \times 2) + 7$

   Ⓒ $(2 + 7) \times 4$

   Ⓓ $(2 \times 4) + (7 \div 3)$

3. Nancy earned $14 washing dishes and $25 washing clothes. Her brother, Duncan, also completed some chores, but Nancy earned triple the amount Duncan earned. Choose the expression that shows how many dollars Duncan earned.

   Ⓐ $(14 + 25) \div 3$

   Ⓑ $(14 \times 25) \div 3$

   Ⓒ $(3 \times 14) - (3 \times 25)$

   Ⓓ $(14 + 25) \times 3$

4. On Tuesday, Dante walked 7 laps and then ran 8 laps around a school track. Dante wrote this expression to show the number of laps he completed on Monday.

   $$(7 + 8) \div 5$$

   Which statement **best** describes the relationship between the number of laps Dante completed on Monday and the number of laps he completed on Tuesday?

   Ⓐ Dante completed 5 times as many laps on Monday as he completed on Tuesday.

   Ⓑ Dante completed 5 more laps on Monday than he completed on Tuesday.

   Ⓒ Dante completed $\frac{1}{5}$ as many laps on Monday as he completed on Tuesday.

   Ⓓ Dante completed 5 fewer laps on Monday than he completed on Tuesday.

5. Compare these expressions.

   Expression 1: $384 \div 192$
   Expression 2: $2 \times (384 \div 192)$
   Expression 3: $0.5 \times (384 \div 192)$

   Which statement is **not** true?

   Ⓐ The value of Expression 1 is two times the value of Expression 2.

   Ⓑ The value of Expression 3 is one-half the value of Expression 1.

   Ⓒ The value of Expression 2 is two times the value of Expression 1.

   Ⓓ The value of Expression 1 is one-half the value of Expression 2.

★ assessment

1. Emma read this phrase.

   "the quotient of 96 divided by the difference between 10 and 2"

   Which expression **best** represents the phrase Emma read?

   Ⓐ $96 \div (10 \div 2)$ Ⓒ $96 \div (10 - 2)$

   Ⓑ $96 \div (10 \times 2)$ Ⓓ $96 \div (10 + 2)$

2. Rabiah likes jelly beans, but she only eats pink and green ones. Rabiah counted 25 pink jelly beans and 41 green jelly beans in a bag of Jolly Jellies. She wrote this expression to show the number of pink and green jelly beans she counted in a bag of Rainbow Jellies.

   $$0.5 \times (25 + 41)$$

   Which statement about Rabiah's jelly beans is true?

   Ⓐ There were 5 times as many pink and green jelly beans in the bag of Rainbow Jellies as in the bag of Jolly Jellies.

   Ⓑ There were half as many pink and green jelly beans in the bag of Rainbow Jellies as in the bag of Jolly Jellies.

   Ⓒ There were twice as many pink and green jelly beans in the bag of Rainbow Jellies as in the bag of Jolly Jellies.

   Ⓓ There were one-fifth as many pink and green jelly beans in the bag of Rainbow Jellies as in the bag of Jolly Jellies.

3. Compare these expressions.

   Expression 1: $54 + 42$

   Expression 2: $(54 + 42) \div 2$

   Expression 3: $(54 + 42) \div 4$

   Which statement is true?

   Ⓐ The value of Expression 1 is one-half the value of Expression 2.

   Ⓑ The value of Expression 3 is two times the value of Expression 2.

   Ⓒ The value of Expression 2 is one-half the value of Expression 1.

   Ⓓ The value of Expression 3 is four times the value of Expression 1.

4. Mr. Jackson bought lunch for his family. His two sons and one daughter each ordered a ham sandwich and a bag of chips. Mr. Jackson decided to order only a ham sandwich for himself. Each sandwich costs $3, and bags of chips are $1 each. Which expression can be used to find the total amount, in dollars, Mr. Jackson paid for the meal?

   Ⓐ $(3 \times 3) + (3 \times 1)$

   Ⓑ $(3 \times 3) + (4 \times 1)$

   Ⓒ $(4 \times 3) + (4 \times 1)$

   Ⓓ $(4 \times 3) + (3 \times 1)$

5. The cost of groceries for Marissa's family is $156 per week. The cost of gasoline for her family is $54 per week. Write an expression to determine the amount of money Marissa's family spends on groceries and gasoline in four weeks.

   Answer: _____

Name _____

Analysis/Analyze

1. Shaun's study group made a rectangular board game for a literature project. They covered the outside edges of the game board with green tape. Their math teacher asked each group member to write an expression representing the total length of green tape the group used. This chart shows the expressions the students wrote.

Student	Expression
Shaun	2 × (18.5 in + 24.25 in)
Makena	18.5 in + 18.5 in + 24.25 in + 24.25 in
Shazeem	18.5 in × 24.25 in
Jackson	(2 × 18.5 in) + (2 × 24.25 in)

Which member of Shaun's study group was incorrect?   **Answer:** _____
Explain your answer.

_____

_____

Synthesis/Create

2. During a math activity, Julio chose these 3 operations cards and 4 number cards from a stack of cards.

| Add | Product | Increased by | 5 | 7 | 3 | 2 |

Use numbers and symbols to write an expression based on the cards Julio drew.

_____

Write a real world situation that could be represented by your expression.

_____

_____

Journal: Analysis/Analyze

List three things you do in which the order of the steps is important.

_____

Why does order affect some activities and not others? How is math like that?

_____

_____

★ motivation station

Expression Tic-Tac-Toe

Play *Expression Tic-Tac-Toe* with a partner. Choose one player to be X and one player to be O. The partner who is X plays first. In turn, each player selects a problem from the list. The player finds an expression on the Tic-Tac-Toe board that matches the problem and marks the space with an X or an O. Next to the problem list, the player records the expression and writes the letter X or O to indicate that the problem has been used. Players may only choose problems that have not been used. The winner is the first player to get three in a row horizontally, vertically, or diagonally.

$(20 \div 2) - 3$	$(8 \div 4) - 2$	$4 \times (9 - 3)$
$(3 \times 3) - 4$	$(8 \times 2) - 4$	$4 \times (8 \times 2)$
$20 + (2 \times 3)$	$9 \times (3 \times 4)$	$(20 - 2) \div 3$

Problem	Expression	Letter
Write an expression for each of the following:		
EXAMPLE: Add 4 and 9. Then multiply by 3.	$3 \times (4 + 9)$	X
Triple three and then subtract 4.		
Multiply 3 and 4. Then multiply by 9.		
Subtract 3 from 9. Then multiply by 4.		.
Divide 20 by 2. Then subtract 3.		
Subtract 2 from 20. Then divide by 3.		
Multiply 2 and 3. Then add 20.		
Double 8 and then subtract 4.		
Divide 8 by 4. Then subtract 2.		
Multiply 8 and 2. Then multiply by 4.		

Parent Activities

1. Find a recipe for your child's favorite dish, and have your child write expressions to show how much is needed to make various amounts of the recipe. For example, if a cookie recipe uses $2\frac{1}{2}$ cups flour, $1\frac{1}{4}$ cups sugar and $\frac{1}{2}$ cup brown sugar, your child would write $3 \times (2\frac{1}{2} + 1\frac{1}{4} + \frac{1}{2})$ to show the total number of cups of these ingredients needed to triple the recipe. Discuss the meanings of "doubling," "tripling," "halving," etc.

2. Ask your child to write an addition expression, such as $20 + 30$, to show the number of minutes spent on math and reading homework in an evening. Then ask your child to write an expression, such as $4 \times (20 + 30)$, to represent the number of minutes that would be spent in 4 evenings if homework takes the same amount of time each day. This activity can be extended to represent the minutes spent on homework in 8 days, one month, etc.

 Level 5

Name _____

1. Kenda started at 0 and completed a pattern following the rule "Add 2." Teddie started at 0 and completed a pattern following the rule "Add 4." Fill in the blanks to show Kenda's and Teddie's patterns.

Kenda: 0, _____, _____, _____, _____

Teddie: 0, _____, _____, _____, _____

2. Look at the patterns in problem 1. How does each term in Teddie's pattern compare to the corresponding term in Kenda's pattern?

Answer: _____

_____

3. Use the corresponding terms from Kenda's and Teddie's patterns to complete these ordered pairs. Then graph the ordered pairs on the coordinate plane.

(0, 0); (2, 4); (4, __); (__, __); (__, __)

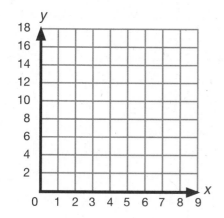

4. Bryan and Trey each bought a coin bank. Bryan put 3 quarters in his bank. Trey put 1 quarter in his bank. Each day, Bryan added 3 more quarters to his bank, and Trey added 1 more quarter to his bank. Complete this table to show the total number of quarters in their banks each day.

Numbers of Quarters Saved

	Day 1	Day 2	Day 3	Day 4	Day 5
Bryan	3				
Trey	1				

How does each term in Bryan's pattern compare to the corresponding term in Trey's pattern?

_____

_____

5. Use the data for the number of quarters saved by Bryan and Trey to complete these ordered pairs. Then graph the ordered pairs on this coordinate plane.

(3, 1); (__, __); (__, __); (__, __); (__, __)

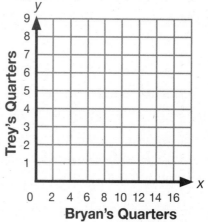

Words for the Wise

axis	ordered pair	term
coordinate plane	pattern rule	x-axis
corresponding terms	sequence	y-axis

partner practice

Use this information to answer questions 1 – 4.

On Monday, Guy and Bess each start saving money for new video games. Guy saves $2 each day mowing lawns. Bess saves $3 each day babysitting.

1. Which table shows the total amount of money Guy and Bess each saved in the first four days?

Ⓐ

	Day 1	Day 2	Day 3	Day 4
Guy	$3	$6	$9	$12
Bess	$2	$4	$6	$8

Ⓑ

	Day 1	Day 2	Day 3	Day 4
Guy	$2	$5	$8	$11
Bess	$3	$5	$7	$9

Ⓒ

	Day 1	Day 2	Day 3	Day 4
Guy	$2	$3	$6	$9
Bess	$4	$6	$8	$12

Ⓓ

	Day 1	Day 2	Day 3	Day 4
Guy	$2	$4	$6	$8
Bess	$3	$6	$9	$12

2. Which shows how each term in Bess's pattern compares to the corresponding term in Guy's pattern?

Ⓐ The numbers in Bess's pattern are 1 more than the numbers in Guy's pattern.

Ⓑ The numbers in Bess's pattern are 2 times as much as the numbers in Guy's pattern.

Ⓒ The numbers in Bess's pattern are $1\frac{1}{2}$ times as much as the numbers in Guy's pattern.

Ⓓ The numbers in Bess's pattern are 1 less than the numbers in Guy's pattern.

3. Guy formed ordered pairs from the corresponding terms in the table. He graphed the ordered pairs on a coordinate plane. Which shows a correct graph for this data?

Ⓐ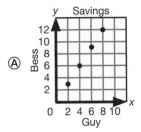

Ⓑ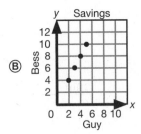

Ⓒ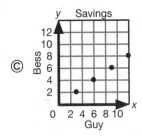

Ⓓ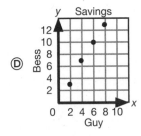

4. Which of the following is **not** an ordered pair on Guy's graph?

Ⓐ (8, 12)   Ⓒ (2, 3)

Ⓑ (6, 10)   Ⓓ (4, 6)

          Level 5

Use this information to answer questions 1 – 5.

At his birthday party on July 1, Jay received a $20 gift card to his favorite restaurant, Hamburger Heaven. Jay ate lunch at Hamburger Heaven on July 5, four days after his birthday, and continued to eat lunch there on days of the month that formed a pattern of "Add 4." Jay always spent exactly $5 for lunch.

1. Which table shows the pattern of the days of the month and the balances, in dollars, on Jay's gift card after eating at Hamburger Heaven?

Ⓐ
Gift Card Balance

Day of the Month	Balance ($)
1	20
4	15
7	10
10	5
13	0

Ⓒ
Gift Card Balance

Day of the Month	Balance ($)
1	20
5	16
9	12
13	8
17	4

Ⓑ
Gift Card Balance

Day of the Month	Balance ($)
20	1
15	5
10	9
5	13
0	17

Ⓓ
Gift Card Balance

Day of the Month	Balance ($)
1	20
5	15
9	10
13	5
17	0

2. Which shows the pattern rule for the balance on Jay's gift card?

Ⓐ Add 5.

Ⓑ Subtract 5.

Ⓒ Subtract 4.

Ⓓ Add 4.

3. Which statement is true about the balances on Jay's gift card?

Ⓐ The value of Jay's card increases with each day of the month.

Ⓑ Jay can also use his gift card to pay for lunches on July 21 and July 25.

Ⓒ Jay had a lower balance on his gift card on July 9 than on July 13.

Ⓓ Jay spent all the money on his gift card for four lunches at Hamburger Heaven

4. Which shows ordered pairs from the corresponding terms for the days of the month and the balances on the gift card?

Ⓐ (1, 20), (5, 15), (9, 10), (13, 5), (17, 0)

Ⓑ (17, 20), (13, 15), (9, 10), (5, 5), (1, 0)

Ⓒ (17, 0), (14, 5), (11, 10), (8, 15)

Ⓓ (1, 5), (9, 13), (17, 20), (15, 10), (5, 0)

5. Jay graphed the ordered pairs on this coordinate plane.

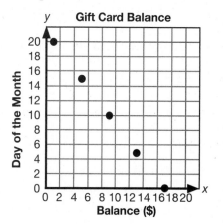

What mistake did Jay make?

Ⓐ Jay incorrectly plotted the point (9, 10).

Ⓑ Jay's graph should have extended to 31 since there are 31 days in July.

Ⓒ Jay wrote the wrong labels on the x-axis and the y-axis.

Ⓓ Jay incorrectly plotted the point (17, 0).

Name _____

Use this information to answer questions 1 – 5.

Maddie started at 0 and completed a pattern following the rule "Add 3." Ariel started at 0 and completed a pattern following the rule "Add 6."

1. What are the first 5 terms of Maddie's and Ariel's patterns?

   Ⓐ Maddie: 0, 3, 9, 12, 15
      Ariel: 0, 6, 12, 18, 24

   Ⓑ Maddie: 0, 3, 6, 9, 12
      Ariel: 0, 6, 12, 18, 24

   Ⓒ Maddie: 0, 3, 6, 9, 12
      Ariel: 0, 6, 9, 12, 15

   Ⓓ Maddie: 0, 3, 9, 12, 15
      Ariel: 0, 2, 4, 6, 8

2. Maddie correctly recorded ordered pairs using the corresponding terms of her pattern and Ariel's pattern. Which shows the ordered pairs Maddie wrote?

   Ⓐ (0, 3), (6, 9), (12, 0), (6, 12), (18, 24)

   Ⓑ (0, 0), (6, 3), (12, 6), (9, 18), (12, 24)

   Ⓒ (0, 0), (3, 3), (6, 6), (9, 9), (12, 12)

   Ⓓ (0, 0), (3, 6), (6, 12), (9, 18), (12, 24)

3. Which is a correct statement about the two girls' patterns?

   Ⓐ The sixth term of Maddie's pattern will be greater than the sixth term of Ariel's pattern.

   Ⓑ The sixth term of Ariel's pattern will be less than the sixth term of Maddie's pattern.

   Ⓒ The sixth term of Maddie's pattern will be less than the sixth term of Ariel's pattern.

   Ⓓ The sixth term of Ariel's pattern will be equal to the sixth term of Maddie's pattern.

4. Which shows the relationship between the terms of Maddie's pattern and the corresponding terms of Ariel's pattern?

   Ⓐ The terms in Maddie's pattern are two times as much as the corresponding terms in Ariel's pattern.

   Ⓑ The terms in Ariel's pattern are half as much as the corresponding terms in Maddie's pattern.

   Ⓒ The terms in Ariel's pattern are two times as much as the corresponding terms in Maddie's pattern.

   Ⓓ The terms in Ariel's pattern are three times as much as the corresponding terms in Maddie's pattern.

5. Graph the ordered pairs created from the corresponding terms of Maddie's and Ariel's patterns on this coordinate plane. Be sure to include labels for the *x*-axis and the *y*-axis.

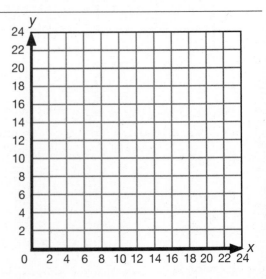

Name _____

Analysis/Analyze

1. Carmela and her little brother, Paolo, are saving money to buy a video game system. Carmela saves $8 every week from her babysitting job. Paolo saves $2 every week from his job walking dogs. Carmela and Paolo record their total earnings on a table.

Week	Carmela	Paolo	Together
1	$8	$2	$10
2	$16	$4	$20
3	$24	$6	$30
4	$32	$8	$40
5	$40	$10	$50
6	$48	$12	$60

Describe 3 patterns you find in Carmela and Paolo's table.

1. _____

2. _____

3. _____

Analysis/Analyze

2. Isabel's house has a pink bathroom and a blue bathroom. Each bathroom has a bathtub with a capacity of 50 gallons. Isabel fills each bathtub to the top and then sets a timer to determine how quickly each tub drains. The tub in the pink bathroom drains 5 gallons every 10 seconds. The tub in the blue bathroom drains twice as fast as the tub in the pink bathroom. Isabel graphs the drain times for each bathtub on this grid.

Help Isabel by filling in the words "Pink" or "Blue" to label the line segments on the grid. Then write a sentence to explain your answers.

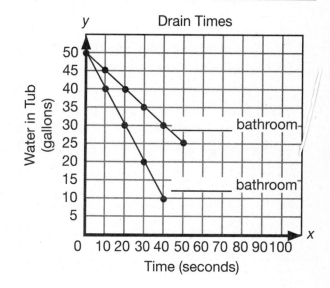

_____

_____

_____

Journal: Analysis/Analyze

What tips could you give to fourth-grade students to help them graph ordered pairs on the coordinate plane?

_____

_____

_____

Toothpick Patterns

Use toothpicks to create a pattern of triangles and a pattern of squares as shown.

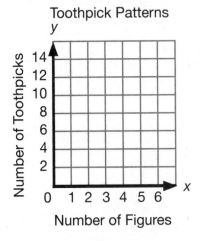

Pattern A   **Pattern B**

Complete these tables to record the two different patterns you formed.

Pattern A - Triangles	
Number of Triangles	Number of Toothpicks
1	
2	
3	
4	

Pattern B - Squares	
Number of Squares	Number of Toothpicks
1	
2	
3	
4	

Use this coordinate plane to graph the ordered pairs found for Pattern A. Then use the same coordinate plane to graph the ordered pairs found for Pattern B.

Toothpick Patterns

Number of Toothpicks (y-axis): 2, 4, 6, 8, 10, 12, 14

Number of Figures (x-axis): 0 1 2 3 4 5 6

Describe how the numbers of toothpicks in the two patterns compare. _____

_____

Parent Activities

1. Play a game using coordinates, such as Battleship. Show your child how coordinates are also used when reading maps.

2. Work together to complete the table comparing how many times your child breathes and how many times your child's heart beats every 10 seconds, every 20 seconds, and so on. Determine if there is a regular pattern or if any comparisons can be made between the two sets of data.

Number of Seconds	Number of Breaths	Number of Heartbeats
10		
20		
30		

Name _____

1. Madea wrote this number.

   156.389

   Write a number that contains an 8 with a value 10 times as much as the 8 in Madea's number and a 5 that has a value one-tenth as much as the 5 in Madea's number.

   Answer: _____

2. Look at these numbers:

   0.3, 0.103, 0.13

   Which number has the digit 3 in the place with the greatest value?

   Answer: _____

3. This table shows the discounts for different prices at a sale.

Original Price ($)	Discount ($)
23.84	2.38
37.92	3.79
41.93	4.19

   Explain the relationship between the value of the digits in the original price and the value of the digits in the discount.

   Answer: _____

   _____

4. Select a digit between 1 and 9. Use the digit repeatedly to create a 5-digit number in this place value chart.

hundreds	tens	ones	•	tenths	hundredths
			•		

   How does the value of the digit in the tenths place compare to the value of the digit in the hundredths place?

   Answer: _____

   _____

   How does the value of the digit in the tens place compare to the value of the digit in the hundreds place?

   Answer: _____

   _____

   How does the value of the digit in the ones place compare to the value of the digit in the place to its right?

   Answer: _____

   _____

5. Fill in the blanks.

   The number 2000 is _____ times as much as the number 200.

   The number 0.5 is _____ as much as the number 5.

Words for the Wise

decimal number	hundredth
decimal point	place value
digit	tenth

thousandth

Use your brain on this one!

partner practice

1. Shelley purchased several stuffed animals to give to charity. The price of each animal is listed in the chart.

Animal	Purchase Price
Bear	$4.95
Horse	$5.94
Duck	$3.56
Dog	$14.67
Caterpillar	$16.25

Which stuffed animal contains a 5 with a value that is $\frac{1}{10}$ the value of the 5 in the purchase price of the horse?

Ⓐ bear

Ⓒ dog

Ⓑ duck

Ⓓ caterpillar

2. Minh is interested in baseball statistics. This year, he collected batting averages for his favorite players.

1. Jose Reyes, NYM	0.337
2. Ryan Braun, MIL	0.332
3. Matt Kemp, LAD	0.324
4. Hunter Pence, HOU/PHI	0.314
5. Joey Votto, CIN	0.309

Which comparison about the averages of Ryan Braun and Matt Kemp is true?

Ⓐ The value of the 2 in Ryan's batting average is $\frac{1}{10}$ the value of the 2 in Matt's batting average.

Ⓑ The value of the 2 in Matt's batting average is $\frac{1}{10}$ the value of the 2 in Ryan's batting average.

Ⓒ The value of the 2 in Ryan's batting average is 10 times greater than the value of the 2 in Matt's batting average.

Ⓓ The value of the 2 in Ryan's batting average is equal to the value of the 2 in Matt's batting average.

3. In the number 777.77, each digit is a 7, but the value of each digit is different based on its placement. How does the value of the 7 in the tenths place compare to the value of the 7 directly above the arrow?

7	7	7	•	7	7

Ⓐ The value of the 7 in the tenths place is one time as much.

Ⓑ The value of the 7 in the tenths place is ten times as much.

Ⓒ The value of the 7 in the tenths place is $\frac{1}{10}$ as much.

Ⓓ The value of the 7 in the tenths place is $\frac{1}{100}$ as much.

4. Last summer, Jon earned $916.55 mowing lawns. His brother made $91.65 completing chores at home. Compare the value of the 9 in each of the two numbers. How do the values of the digits compare?

Ⓐ The value of the 9 in Jon's number is 100 times the value of the 9 in his brother's number.

Ⓑ The value of the 9 in Jon's number is 10 times the value of the 9 in his brother's number.

Ⓒ The value of the 9 in Jon's number is the same as the value of the 9 in his brother's number.

Ⓓ The value of the 9 in Jon's number is $\frac{1}{10}$ the value of the 9 in his brother's number.

5. How does the value of 2 dimes compare to the value of 2 dollars?

Ⓐ The value of 2 dimes is 10 times as much.

Ⓑ The value of 2 dimes is 20 times as much.

Ⓒ The value of 2 dimes is $\frac{1}{10}$ as much.

Ⓓ The value of 2 dimes is $\frac{1}{20}$ as much.

     Level 5

1. Mona is the manager at a pizza parlor. She made this table to record the numbers of pizzas purchased with a coupon and the numbers purchased at the regular price.

Month	Number with Coupon	Number at Regular Price
June	861	1387
July	923	2212
August	1087	1107
September	1346	1002
October	2548	938

Which has a 1 with a value that is $\frac{1}{10}$ the value of the 1 in the number of August's coupon purchases?

Ⓐ June's coupon purchase

Ⓑ June's regular price

Ⓒ July's regular price

Ⓓ August's regular price

2. Study these decimal models.

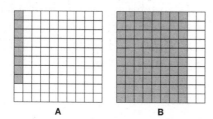

A   B

Compare the shaded area of A to the shaded area of B. How do the values compare?

Ⓐ A has a value 10 times as much as B.

Ⓑ A has a value 100 times as much as B.

Ⓒ A has a value $\frac{1}{10}$ as much as B.

Ⓓ A has a value $\frac{1}{100}$ as much as B.

3. Charlotte has $435.21 in her savings account. Which of these numbers has a 5 with a value that is $\frac{1}{10}$ the value of the 5 in 435.21?

Ⓐ 356.79   Ⓒ 1073.56

Ⓑ 532.01   Ⓓ 1349.05

4. Michael and his parents ate dinner at Pepper's. Their total bill, before tip, was $42.94. Michael's father left a $4.29 tip. How does the value of the 9 in the bill compare to the value of the 9 in the tip?

Ⓐ The value of the 9 in the bill is $\frac{1}{100}$ the value of the 9 in the tip.

Ⓑ The value of the 9 in the bill is $\frac{1}{10}$ the value of the 9 in the tip.

Ⓒ The value of the 9 in the bill is 10 times the value of the 9 in the tip.

Ⓓ The value of the 9 in the bill has the same value as the 9 in the tip.

5. Casey is planning his fantasy baseball league for next year. He collected data for the earned run average of several players as shown on this chart.

Name of Player/Team	Earned Run Average (ERA)
1. Clayton Kershaw, LAD	2.28
2. Roy Halladay, PHI	2.35
3. Cliff Lee, PHI	2.40
4. Ryan Vogelsong, SF	2.71
5. Tim Lincecum, SF	2.74

How does the digit 4 in Cliff Lee's earned run average compare to the digit 4 in Tim Lincecum's earned run average?

Ⓐ The 4 in Cliff's ERA has a value $\frac{1}{10}$ as much as the 4 in Tim's ERA.

Ⓑ The 4 in Cliff's ERA has a value 10 times as much as the 4 in Tim's ERA.

Ⓒ The 4 in Tim's ERA has a value 10 times as much as the 4 in Cliff's ERA.

Ⓓ The 4 in Tim's ERA has the same value as the 4 in Cliff's ERA.

assessment

1. This table shows the high scores for the top 5 players on a video game.

Player	Score
Player 1	401,987
Player 2	359,847
Player 3	321,795
Player 4	297,634
Player 5	972,863

Which contains a 9 with a value 10 times as much as the 9 in Player 2's score?

Ⓐ 972,863

Ⓑ 321,795

Ⓒ 357,849

Ⓓ 297,634

2. How does the value of 6 one-dollar bills compare to the value of 6 dimes?

Ⓐ It is 10 times as much as 6 dimes.

Ⓑ It is $\frac{1}{10}$ the value of 6 dimes.

Ⓒ It is 6 times as much as 6 dimes.

Ⓓ It is 60 times as much as 6 dimes.

3. The volume of a cylinder is 5.024 cubic inches. Which number contains a 4 with a value 10 times as much as the 4 in 5.024?

Ⓐ 13.704

Ⓑ 8.245

Ⓒ 4.01

Ⓓ 0.46

4. Jennifer and Julie sold cookies for their school. Jennifer's sales totaled $475.00, while Julie's totaled $47.50. Which statement is **not** correct?

Ⓐ The 4 in Jennifer's sales has a value 10 times as much as the 4 in Julie's sales.

Ⓑ The 7 in Julie's sales has a value $\frac{1}{10}$ as much as the 7 in Jennifer's sales.

Ⓒ The 4 in Jennifer's sales has a value 100 times as much as the 4 in Julie's sales.

Ⓓ The 5 in Jennifer's sales has a value 10 times as much as the 5 in Julie's sales.

5. Jacob collected 127 pounds of aluminum cans for a recycling project at his school. Barbara collected 210 pounds for the same project. How is the value of the 2 in Jacob's amount different from the value of the 2 in Barbara's amount?

Answer: _____

Hannah also collected cans. The amount she collected is represented by a 3-digit number with digits 1, 2, and 7. The value of the 2 in Hannah's number is $\frac{1}{10}$ the value of the 2 in Jacob's number. The value of the 1 in Hannah's number is 10 times as much as the value of the 1 in Barbara's number. How many pounds of cans did Hannah collect?

Answer: _____

 Level 5

Name _____

Analysis/Analyze

1. Connie has saved 5 pennies, 5 dimes, 5 one-dollar bills, 5 ten-dollar bills, and 5 hundred-dollar bills. How much money has Connie saved?

   Answer: _____

   How does the value of 5 pennies compare to the value of 5 ten-dollar bills?

   Answer: _____

   How does the value of 5 hundred-dollar bills compare to the value of 5 dimes?

   Answer: _____

Analysis/Analyze

2. Use the clues to find the mystery number. Be sure to place the decimal point in the correct location.

   • The number has 4 digits to the left of the decimal point and 1 digit to the right.

   • One digit is a 2 with the same total value as the 2 in one dozen.

   • One place contains a digit with the same total value as the number of days in the month of June.

   • One digit has a value that is $\frac{1}{100}$ the value of the digit in the tens place.

   • One digit has a value that is 100 times as much as the value of the digit in the ones place.

   • One digit is a 9.

   What is the mystery number?   _____ _____ _____ _____ _____

Journal: Analysis/Analyze

   Give an example of a situation in which you need to understand the values of the digits in a number.

   _____

   _____

   _____

   _____

Diamond Digits

Play *Diamond Digits* with a partner. Each pair of players needs a paper clip and pencil for the spinner, a pencil for writing, and the game board below. In turn, each player spins the spinner, and locates the diamond that has the correct value for the digit. The player claims the diamond by writing his/her name under the diamond. If a diamond has already been claimed, play passes to the next player. The game ends when all of the diamonds have been claimed. The winner is the player who claims the most diamonds.

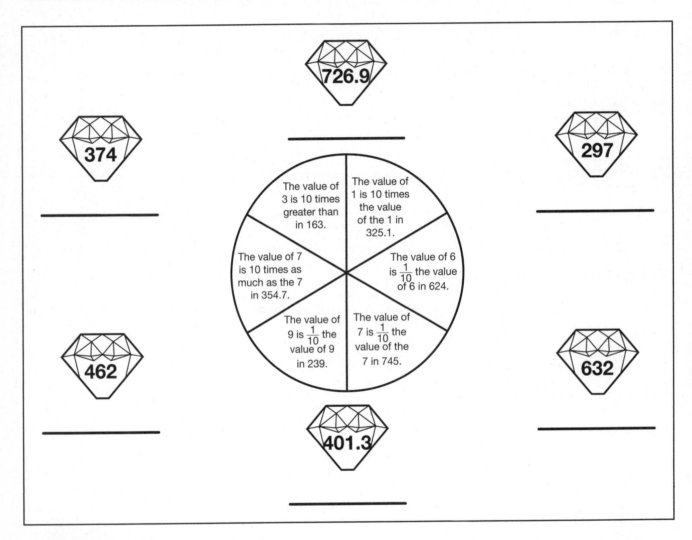

Parent Activities

1. Using a store receipt, have your child underline digits that are the same and explain the relationship between the digits. Use vocabulary such as "10 times as much as" or "$\frac{1}{10}$ as much as."

2. Using play money, provide your child with a $1000 bill, $100 bill, $10 bill, $1 bill, dime, and penny. Ask your child to solve riddles such as, "My value is 10 times as much as the value of a penny. What am I?" (dime) or "My value is $\frac{1}{100}$ the value of a $100 bill. What am I?" (dollar)

     Level 5

Name _____

1. Misaki is solving a math problem. She multiplies 36.5 meters by 1000. How many zeros should be to the left of the decimal point in Misaki's product?

   Answer: _____

2. Juan needs to write an exponent in this expression so the product will have a "1" in the hundred thousands place. Which exponent should Juan write?

   $$140 \times 10^?$$

   Answer: _____

3. The width of a plant cell can be expressed as $6.0 \div 10^2$ millimeters. What number is equal to this expression?

   Answer: _____ mm

4. Tya took a math quiz. The last question asked, "By how many places will the place value of 6.224 increase when multiplied by 10^6?" Tya incorrectly answered 10. What is the correct answer?

   Answer: _____

5. Annalisa was working with powers of ten. She created this table.

Expression	Expression with Exponent	Answer
72 ÷ 1000	$72 \div 10^3$	
72 ÷ 100	$72 \div 10^2$	
72 ÷ 10	$72 \div 10^1$	
72 × 10	72×10^1	720
72 × 100	72×10^2	7,200
72 × 1000	72×10^3	72,000

Annalisa understands how to multiply by powers of ten, but does not know how to divide by powers of ten. Complete the table. Then write a short explanation to help Annalisa understand how to divide by powers of ten.

Answer: _____

_____

Words for the Wise

decimal point	multiple	product
exponent	place value	quotient
factor	power	tenth
hundredth	power of ten	thousandth

The road to success starts here!

partner practice

1. Collin multiplied a decimal number by 1000. The product contained exactly 2 zeros to the left of the decimal point. Which factor could Collin have used?

    Ⓐ 3.6

    Ⓑ 4.87

    Ⓒ 5.0

    Ⓓ 144.183

2. Helena used this table to learn about multiplication by powers of ten.

Factor	Factor	Product
3.99	10^2	399
10.035	10^2	1003.5
3	10^2	300
30	10^2	3000

Helena's conclusions are shown here. Which conclusion is **not** correct?

    Ⓐ The place value of the 3 in the first factor is increased by 2 places when the factor is multiplied by 10^2.

    Ⓑ When any number is multiplied by 100, the product can always be found by affixing 2 zeros to the right side of the number.

    Ⓒ The place value of each digit in a factor is always increased by two places when the factor is multiplied by 10^2.

    Ⓓ When a number is multiplied by a power of 10, the exponent of the 10 tells how many places to the right the decimal will move.

3. Which is **not** equal to 3.2×10^2?

    Ⓐ 3.2×100

    Ⓑ $3.2 \times 10 \times 10$

    Ⓒ 3200

    Ⓓ 320

4. Grayson's class was asked to work this problem.

    $$275 \div 10^2$$

    His teacher picked Grayson to work the problem for the class. Which of these equations could Grayson use?

    Ⓐ $(2.75 \div 10) \div 10 = 275$

    Ⓑ $275 \div 20 = 13.75$

    Ⓒ $275 \div (10 \times 10) = 27.5$

    Ⓓ $(275 \div 10) \div 10 = 2.75$

5. The diameter of our sun, a medium-sized star, can be written as 8.65×10^5 miles. Which shows the diameter of our sun?

    Ⓐ 86,500 mi

    Ⓑ 865,000 mi

    Ⓒ 8,650,000 mi

    Ⓓ 86,500,000 mi

 Level 5

1. While converting units of measure, Apollo and Frank multiplied 3.45 by 10,000. They disagreed on how many zeros were to the left of the decimal point in the answer. Which shows the correct number of zeros in the product?

   Ⓐ 1

   Ⓑ 2

   Ⓒ 3

   Ⓓ 4

2. Shannon is researching ocean trenches for her science project. She finds this chart on the internet.

Ocean Trench	Depth (feet)
Mariana Trench	36,000
Izu-Ogasawara Trench	32,000
Philippine Trench	35,000
Yap Trench	28,000

   For her report, Shannon wants to write the depth of the Philippine Trench using powers of ten. Which expression shows one way to write the number correctly?

   Ⓐ 35×10^4

   Ⓑ 0.35×10^4

   Ⓒ 3.5×10^3

   Ⓓ 3.5×10^4

3. Vincent found 0.8 as the quotient of a division problem. Which expression is equal to this quotient?

   Ⓐ $0.8 \div 10^2$

   Ⓑ $8 \div 10^2$

   Ⓒ $80 \div 10^2$

   Ⓓ $800 \div 10^4$

4. Derrick's aunt gave him $140 for his birthday. Derrick went shopping in the mall with the money. When he returned home and counted his change, Derrick had $1.40 left. Which statement does **not** correctly describe the relationship between $140 and $1.40?

   Ⓐ When the place value of $140 is decreased by two decimal places, the result is $1.40.

   Ⓑ When $140 is divided by 10^2, the quotient is $1.40.

   Ⓒ When $1.40 is multiplied by 100, the product is $140.

   Ⓓ When $140 is divided by (10×2), the quotient is $1.40.

5. Jeremy's dad created a bar graph to show concession stand sales during the first four home basketball games of the season.

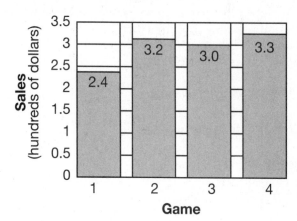

   Jeremy notices the concession sales on the graph represent hundreds of dollars. Which shows the total sales for the four games?

   Ⓐ $1190

   Ⓑ $1100

   Ⓒ $240

   Ⓓ $119

★ assessment

1. Sonya and Steve are working on their math homework. They need to write a number that has the same value as 6.72×10^4. Sonya says the number should have two zeros to the left of the decimal point. Steve disagrees and says the number should have four zeros. Who is correct and why?

   Ⓐ Steve is correct because the exponent 4 indicates how many zeros should be in the answer.

   Ⓑ Steve is correct because a decimal number whose place value is increased by 4 decimal places will always have 4 zeros.

   Ⓒ Sonya is correct because a decimal number whose place value is increased by 4 decimal places will usually have only 2 zeros.

   Ⓓ Sonya is correct because the exponent 4 indicates the decimal point will be moved four places to the right.

2. The speed of sound through water is about 4.9×10^3 feet per second. Which is another way to express this measure?

   Ⓐ 0.049 feet per second

   Ⓑ 490 feet per second

   Ⓒ 4,900 feet per second

   Ⓓ 49,000 feet per second

3. Which is **not** equal to $65.4 \div 10^2$?

   Ⓐ 6.54

   Ⓑ $(65.4 \div 10) \div 10$

   Ⓒ $65.4 \div 100$

   Ⓓ 0.654

4. Reese correctly divided 67 by a power of 10. Her quotient was 0.067. What was the divisor in Reese's equation?

   Ⓐ 10^2

   Ⓑ 10^3

   Ⓒ 10^4

   Ⓓ 10^5

5. The mass of an elephant is approximately 5.1×10^3 kilograms. Which shows a way to find this product?

   Ⓐ Move the decimal point 3 places to the right.

   Ⓑ Move the decimal point 3 places to the left.

   Ⓒ Add 3 zeros to the right of the tenths place.

   Ⓓ Add 2 zeros between the 5 and the 1.

6. Terrence multiplied 20 by a power of 10. His answer contained 4 zeros to the left of the decimal point. What power of ten did Terrence use as a factor in his equation?

   Answer: _____

   Explain how you found your answer.

   Answer: _____

   _____

 Level 5

Analysis/Analyze

1. A group of students competed in a video game tournament. The students recorded their scores as mathematical expressions, using powers of ten, as shown on this chart.

Video Game Tournament	
Name	**Score**
Arnie	$78{,}469 \div 10^2$
Belinda	42.3×10^3
Gavin	352.93×10^2
Zuma	$330{,}007 \div 10^3$

The first place trophy was awarded to the student with the highest score. Write the names of the students on the trophies to show the results of the championship.

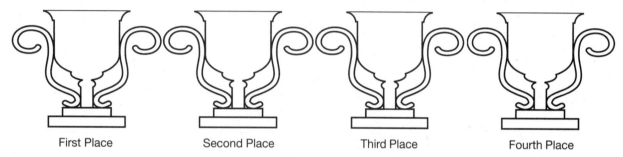

First Place   Second Place   Third Place   Fourth Place

A fifth student, Lola, arrived too late to compete but played video games anyway. She would have won the second place trophy if she had been on time. Write an expression, using powers of 10, to show a score Lola might have earned.

Answer: _____

Analysis/Analyze

2. If $10^2 = 10 \times 10$, what is the value of $(10^2)^2$?

Answer: _____

Explain how you found your answer. _____

_____

Journal: Analysis/Analyze

Explain the difference between multiplying $5 \times (2 \times 10)$ and multiplying 5×10^2.

_____

_____

★ motivation station

Flower Power

Play *Flower Power* with a partner. Each pair of players needs a number cube, two different-colored crayons or markers, and the game sheet. In turn, a player rolls the number cube. If the player rolls an even number, 10^2 is multiplied by the number given for the round as shown on the table. If a player rolls an odd number, 10^3 is multiplied by the number given for the round. Each player writes the product in the table. The players compare the product using the signs $<$, $>$, or $=$. The player with the greatest product colors a flower. If the products are equal, each player colors a flower. The winner is the person who colors the most flowers.

Round	Number	Player 1	$<$, $>$, or $=$	Player 2
1	55			
2	7.5			
3	18			
4	4.5			
5	786			
6	39.2			
7	88.15			
8	4.12			

Parent Activities

1. Ask your child questions about prices at the grocery store if you purchase 10, 100, or 1000 of an item (e.g., "One can of beans costs $0.59. How much will it cost if we purchase 10 cans? How could we find the cost of 100 or 1000 cans without using a calculator?"). Help your child understand that the decimal point will move one, two, or three places to the right each time the price is multiplied by 10, 100, or 1000.

2. Use a trip to the gas station as an opportunity to teach multiplying by 10. Ask your child to notice the price per gallon and then to guess how much ten gallons would cost. After ten gallons have been pumped, ask your child to note the total price. Help your child to see that the decimal has moved one place to the right. Discuss with your child other examples of decimal numbers in the real world and how the placement of the decimal will move to the right or left depending on whether the number is multiplied or divided by a power of ten.

Name _____

1. Peter's coach asked him to weigh on a digital scale. Peter discovered that his weight was one hundred three and four hundredths pounds. Write the decimal number that names Peter's weight.

   Answer: _____

   Write Peter's weight in expanded form.

   Answer: _____

2. Using numbers, words, or pictures, explain why 6.6 is greater than 6.325.

   Answer: _____

   _____

3. Use the digits 5, 8, 0, and 3 to write the three smallest possible decimal numbers in the spaces. Each digit must be used exactly one time in each number.

   ____ • ____ ____ ____

   ____ • ____ ____ ____

   ____ • ____ ____ ____

4. Use <, >, or = to complete this comparison.

   0.17 ◯ 0.170

   Explain your answer. _____

   _____

5. A decimal number is represented by the shaded model. Each completely shaded square represents one whole.

   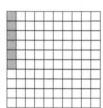

   Write the decimal number for this model in the place value chart.

Tens	Ones	.	Tenths	Hundredths

   Write the decimal number in words.

   Answer: _____

   _____

Words for the Wise

compare/comparison	expanded form
decimal number	greater than (>)
decimal point	hundredth
digit	less than (<)
equal (=)	place value

tenth

thousandth

Give me a high five!

partner practice

1. A dog named Anastasia set a record by popping 100 balloons in 44.49 seconds. Which shows the expanded form of 44.49?

   Ⓐ $(4 \times 10) + (4 \times 1) + (4 \times \frac{1}{10}) + (9 \times \frac{1}{1000})$

   Ⓑ $(40 \times 10) + (4 \times 1) + (4 \times \frac{1}{10}) + (9 \times \frac{1}{100})$

   Ⓒ $(4 \times 10) + (4 \times 1) + (4 \times \frac{1}{10}) + (9 \times \frac{1}{100})$

   Ⓓ $(40 \times 10) + (4 \times 1) + (40 \times \frac{1}{100}) + (9 \times \frac{1}{100})$

2. A meteorologist reports that seven and two hundred five thousandths inches of rain fell during the month of April. Which number should be recorded for April's rainfall?

   Ⓐ 7.025 in

   Ⓑ 7.205 in

   Ⓒ 7.25 in

   Ⓓ 7.250 in

3. Based on this model, which of the following is true?

   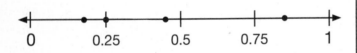

   Ⓐ 0.86 < 0.43

   Ⓑ 0.17 > 0.86

   Ⓒ 0.43 > 0.25

   Ⓓ 0.25 < 0.17

4. Zoe cut lengths of wood to make a picture frame. She cut one piece of wood 43.75 inches long. She cut the other piece so that it was 43.9 inches long. Which sentence **best** explains the relationship between the lengths of the two pieces of wood?

   Ⓐ 43.75 inches is longer because $\frac{75}{100}$ is greater than $\frac{9}{10}$.

   Ⓑ 43.75 inches is shorter because $\frac{75}{1000}$ is less than $\frac{9}{10}$.

   Ⓒ 43.9 inches is longer because $\frac{9}{10}$ is greater than $\frac{7}{10}$.

   Ⓓ 43.9 inches is longer because $\frac{9}{10}$ is less than $\frac{7}{10}$.

5. Mr. Karr resurfaced a sidewalk in the park that was 125.065 meters long. How is this number written in words?

   Ⓐ one hundred twenty-five and sixty-five hundred thousandths

   Ⓑ one hundred twenty-five and sixty-five thousandths

   Ⓒ one hundred twenty-five and sixty-five hundredths

   Ⓓ one hundred twenty-five and sixty-five tenths

6. Which of the following is **not** equal to 0.34?

   Ⓐ $(3 \times \frac{1}{10}) + (4 \times \frac{1}{100})$

   Ⓑ $\frac{340}{1000}$

   Ⓒ $\frac{3}{10} + \frac{4}{100}$

   Ⓓ $0.30 + 0.4$

Level 5

1. Carl's lab group planted bean seeds for a science investigation. The height of each group member's seedling after one week is shown in this chart.

Student	Seedling Height (inches)
Averitt	3.68
Bob	3.625
Carl	3.562
Dahlia	3.8

Which expression does **not** correctly compare the heights of the seedlings?

Ⓐ 3.8 > 3.68

Ⓑ 3.625 > 3.68

Ⓒ 3.562 < 3.8

Ⓓ 3.68 > 3.562

2. Jordan and Dillon are working on a science investigation. Jordan needs to measure 0.075 liter of distilled water. How would this amount be read?

Ⓐ seven and five hundredths

Ⓑ seven and five thousandths

Ⓒ seventy-five hundredths

Ⓓ seventy-five thousandths

3. While at the grocery store, Mitchell weighed one potato on the produce scale. The weight of the potato was 0.34 pound. Which of the following is less than the weight of Mitchell's potato?

Ⓐ $\frac{3}{10} + \frac{4}{1000}$ Ⓒ $(3 \times 1) + (4 \times \frac{1}{10})$

Ⓑ 0.3 + 0.04   Ⓓ $\frac{34}{100}$

4. The world's smallest horse, Einstein, measured 16.24 centimeters tall at birth. Thumbelina, who measured 43.18 centimeters tall, was the smallest horse before Einstein was born. Which shows the expanded form of Einstein's height?

Ⓐ $(1 \times 10) + (6 \times 1) + (2 \times \frac{1}{10}) + (4 \times \frac{1}{100})$

Ⓑ $(1 \times 10) + (6 \times 1) + (2 \times \frac{1}{100}) + (4 \times \frac{1}{1000})$

Ⓒ $(4 \times 10) + (3 \times 1) + (1 \times \frac{1}{10}) + (8 \times \frac{1}{100})$

Ⓓ $(4 \times 10) + (3 \times 1) + (1 \times \frac{1}{100}) + (8 \times \frac{1}{1000})$

5. Jonathan and Anna are organizing their dad's tool box. They place bolts in order from smallest diameter to largest diameter. Jonathan wants to put the 0.624-inch bolt first followed by the 0.75-inch bolt. Anna tells him that the 0.75-inch bolt should be first. Who is correct and why?

Ⓐ Anna is correct. When comparing decimals, the decimal is dropped and the numbers are compared, and 75 is less than 624.

Ⓑ Jonathan is correct. When comparing decimals, the place value of each digit is compared, and $\frac{6}{10}$ is less than $\frac{7}{10}$.

Ⓒ Jonathan is correct. When comparing decimals that have a zero in the ones place, the last digits on the right are compared, and 4 is smaller than 5.

Ⓓ Anna is correct. When comparing decimals, the decimal with fewer digits is the smaller number, and 0.75 has fewer digits than 0.624.

1. The Earth spins on an axis that is tilted about 23.51°. How is this number written in words?

   Ⓐ twenty-three and fifty-one tenths

   Ⓑ twenty-three and fifty-one hundredths

   Ⓒ twenty-two and fifty-one hundredths

   Ⓓ twenty-three and fifty-one thousandths

2. During one regular season, Detroit's Miguel Cabrera led the National League with a batting average of 0.344. Which shows this number written in expanded form?

   Ⓐ $(3 \times 100) + (4 \times 10) + (4 \times 1)$

   Ⓑ $(3 \times 100) + (44 \times 1000)$

   Ⓒ $(3 \times \frac{1}{100}) + (44 \times \frac{1}{1000})$

   Ⓓ $(3 \times \frac{1}{10}) + (4 \times \frac{1}{100}) + (4 \times \frac{1}{1000})$

3. Study this decimal model.

   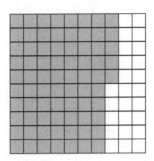

   Which of the following values is equivalent to the number of boxes shaded?

   Ⓐ 0.075   Ⓒ 0.750

   Ⓑ 0.705   Ⓓ 75.0

4. Which comparison is true?

   Ⓐ $0.025 > 0.1$ Ⓒ $0.003 = 0.03$

   Ⓑ $10.004 < 10.03$ Ⓓ $9 < 8.969$

5. Janice records her weight loss on a chart. Using her results from the first five weeks, as shown in her chart, graph Janice's progress on the grid provided.

Week	Pounds Lost
1	1.4
2	1.25
3	0.9
4	1.40
5	1.1

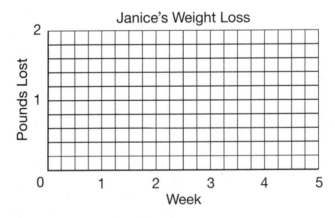

Use the information from the table and the graph to complete these comparisons, using <, >, or = symbols.

Week 1 loss _____ Week 2 loss

Week 3 loss _____ Week 5 loss

Week 4 loss _____ Week 1 loss

Week 2 loss _____ Week 5 loss

Analysis/Analyze

1. Maribelle uses the digits 0, 8, 5, and 3 to write two decimal numbers. She uses each digit only one time in each number. What is the largest number Maribelle could write if 8 is in the tenths place?

   Answer: _____

   What is the smallest number she could write if 8 is in the tenths place?

   Answer: _____

Analysis/Analyze

2. Name 5 decimal numbers that are between 4.78 and 4.79. Explain your answer.

   _____ _____ _____ _____ _____

   _____

   _____

   _____

   _____

Journal: Analysis/Analyze

How is a nickel similar to the decimal number 0.05? How are other coins related to decimal numbers?

_____

_____

_____

_____

motivation station

Decimal Dialogue

Play *Decimal Dialogue* with a partner. Each pair of players needs one game board, two number cubes or dot cubes, and a supply of game markers such as colored centimeter cubes (a different color for each player). Player 1 rolls the two number or dot cubes and chooses a row and column to correspond with the numbers rolled (e.g., 3 and 5 or 5 and 3). At the intersection of the row and column, the player must correctly read aloud the decimal number written in the square (e.g., 3.8 is read as three and eight tenths). If the player is correct, he/she places a game marker on the square, and play passes to Player 2. If the player is incorrect, he/she loses that turn, and play passes to Player 2. If the player rolls two numbers and the resulting squares are already claimed, the player loses that turn. The winner is the player with the most squares covered when the teacher calls time.

	1	2	3	4	5	6
6	1.13	0.1	97.4	0.18	13.13	0.03
5	0.07	0.11	0.8	70.7	0.5	8.65
4	0.7	13.07	0.18	0.2	0.08	8.76
3	0.35	3.7	0.01	6.16	0.67	0.6
2	0.3	14.07	0.74	5.55	0.88	0.02
1	5.8	0.90	0.4	49.51	0.9	10.01

Parent Activities

1. Using the internet, find a list of exchange rates comparing the U.S. dollar to various foreign currencies. For example, dollar to Swiss franc = 0.934, dollar to Canadian dollar = 1.018, and so on. Ask your child to write comparisons between the rates using > (greater than), < (less than) or = (e.g., 0.934 < 1.018).

2. When writing checks to pay bills, allow your child to see how the number is written in both word form and decimal form. Let them "write checks" on blank checks to practice using word form and number form.

 Level 5

Name _____

1. Place a dot on the approximate location of 12.369 on the number line.

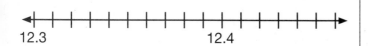

12.3   12.4

What is 12.369 rounded to the nearest tenth?

Answer: _____

2. The large square represents one whole. Cecily shaded the square to represent a decimal number.

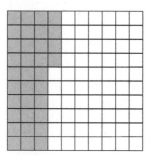

What is the value of Cecily's number rounded to the nearest tenth?

Answer: _____

3. Omar ran the 40-yard dash in 8.746 seconds. What is Omar's time rounded to the nearest hundredth of a second?

Answer: _____

4. Jeremiah rounded a number to 8.7. What could the original number have been?

Answer: _____

_____

5. Violet looked through a catalog and found a dress she wanted to order. She used a calculator to determine that the total cost of the dress, tax, and shipping was $129.207. What is the total rounded to the nearest penny?

Answer: _____

Explain how you found your answer. _____

_____

_____

_____

6. Smith City received 2.45 inches of rain on Monday and 1.72 inches of rain on Tuesday. Write an equation showing a way to estimate, to the nearest inch, the total rainfall for the two days.

Answer: _____

Words for the Wise

approximate	estimate	round
decimal number	hundredth	tenth
decimal point	place value	thousandth

You're catching on now!

partner practice

1. The large square represents one whole. Haley shaded a decimal number in the square as shown.

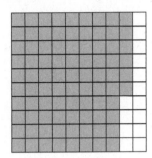

Which shows the value of Haley's number rounded to the nearest whole number?

Ⓐ 0 Ⓒ 1.0

Ⓑ 0.5 Ⓓ 1.5

2. Arnold wants to make sure he saves enough money to purchase a new video game. His mom reminds him to include sales tax. Arnold uses a calculator and finds that he must save a total of $56.987. Which shows this amount rounded to the nearest cent?

Ⓐ $57.00 Ⓒ $56.98

Ⓑ $56.99 Ⓓ $56.90

3. A weather station's location was rounded to 0.11 kilometers above sea level. Which of the following could represent the actual location of the weather station in kilometers above sea level?

Ⓐ 0.117 km Ⓒ 0.102 km

Ⓑ 0.105 km Ⓓ 0.1009 km

4. A carpet beetle is 0.063 inches in length, and a powder post beetle is 0.25 inches in length. Which expression shows a way to estimate the difference in the lengths, to the nearest tenth of an inch, of the two beetles?

Ⓐ 0.063 − 0.25

Ⓑ 0.25 − 0.06

Ⓒ 0.2 − 0.1

Ⓓ 0.3 − 0.1

5. Xavier weighs 44.455 kilograms. Which shows his weight, in kilograms, rounded to the nearest hundredth and the nearest tenth?

Ⓐ 44.40, 44.4

Ⓑ 44.45, 44.5

Ⓒ 44.46, 44.5

Ⓓ 44.50, 44.5

6. Liang runs cross-country track. His best times for his last 3 meets are shown in the table.

Date	Time
June 5	12.10 min
June 12	12.224 min
June 17	11.501 min

Which point on the number line shows Liang's time on June 12, rounded to the nearest hundredth of a minute?

Ⓐ M Ⓒ O

Ⓑ N Ⓓ P

 Level 5

1. Cassandra represented a decimal number with these decimal squares.

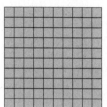 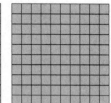 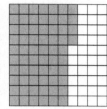

   Which shows Cassandra's number rounded to the nearest tenth?

   Ⓐ 2.0

   Ⓑ 2.6

   Ⓒ 2.65

   Ⓓ 2.7

2. Destiny paid $1.59 for a new school box. What is the price of the school box rounded to the nearest dollar?

   Ⓐ $1.00

   Ⓑ $1.50

   Ⓒ $1.60

   Ⓓ $2.00

3. Carlos helps his mom bake bread. He weighs flour on a digital kitchen scale. The weight of the flour is 13.23 ounces. What is 13.23 rounded to the nearest whole number?

   Ⓐ 12

   Ⓑ 13

   Ⓒ 13.2

   Ⓓ 14

4. Seamus uses a calculator to divide 256 by 19. The calculator shows the quotient to be 13.473. Which shows the quotient rounded to the nearest tenth and the nearest hundredth?

   Ⓐ 13.0, 13.50

   Ⓑ 13.40, 13.46

   Ⓒ 13.5, 13.47

   Ⓓ 13.57, 13.48

5. Monica uses the digits 5, 6, and 7 to make a number. Her number rounds to 6.6. Which of the following numbers could be Monica's number?

   Ⓐ 7.65

   Ⓑ 6.75

   Ⓒ 6.57

   Ⓓ 5.67

6. The chart shows the scores of the top four gymnasts in a recent gymnastics meet.

   Gymnastics Scores

Name	Score
Sarah	9.63
Angela	9.66
Judy	9.54
Tameka	9.57

   Which two gymnasts would have the same score if the scores were rounded to the nearest tenth?

   Ⓐ Sarah and Angela

   Ⓑ Angela and Tameka

   Ⓒ Judy and Tameka

   Ⓓ Sarah and Tameka

★ assessment

1. The large square represents one whole. Tremaine shaded a decimal number in the square as shown.

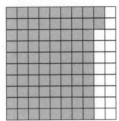

Which shows Tremaine's number rounded to the nearest tenth?

Ⓐ 0.8   Ⓒ 0.9

Ⓑ 0.85   Ⓓ 1.0

2. Emsley is 12.53 miles from her house. Which shows the value of 12.53 rounded to the nearest tenth and the nearest whole number?

Ⓐ 12.0, 13.0   Ⓒ 12.6, 10

Ⓑ 12.5, 13   Ⓓ 12.53, 12

3. Ms. Jones used 591 kilowatt hours of electricity in May. The cost for electricity is $0.091 per kilowatt hour. Her total cost is $53.781, but her bill is rounded to the nearest cent. How much is Ms. Jones' electric bill?

Ⓐ $54.00   Ⓒ $53.78

Ⓑ $53.80   Ⓓ $53.70

4. Natalie's parents are planning a trip. They created this chart showing the average gasoline prices in the nation.

Gasoline Prices

	Regular	Mid-Grade	Premium
Average Price	$3.387	$3.529	$3.663

Which shows the price of mid-grade gasoline rounded to the nearest hundredth?

Ⓐ $3.50   Ⓒ $3.53

Ⓑ $3.52   Ⓓ $3.60

5. The table shows the top five NBA players in field goal percentages for the season. The percentages are shown to the nearest thousandth. Complete the table by rounding each field goal percentage to the nearest tenth and the nearest hundredth.

Player Name	Field Goal Percentage	Field Goal Percentage (nearest tenth)	Field Goal Percentage (nearest hundredth)
Hamady N'Diaye, WAS	0.800		
DeAndre Jordan, LAC	0.686		
Marcus Cousin, UTA	0.667		
Shaquille O'Neal, BOS	0.667		
Jeremy Evans, UTA	0.661		

Why do you think the field goal percentages were extended to the thousandths place rather than stopping at the tenths or hundredths place?

Answer: _____

_____

Application/ Apply

1. Steve rounded a decimal number to the nearest hundredth.

   What is the smallest number he could round to 0.05?

   Answer: _____

   What is the largest number Steve could round to 0.05?

   Answer: _____

Analysis/Analyze

2. Sue is thinking of a decimal number that will fill these blanks:

   ____ ____ . ____ ____

   What is a number that will round to 18 if rounded to the nearest whole number and to 17.5 if rounded to the nearest tenth?

   Answer: _____

Journal: Analysis/Analyze

Describe a situation in everyday life in which you use rounding to estimate.

_____

_____

_____

_____

Secret Code Wheel

Solve problems for A-Z and write the answers in the inner section of the secret code wheel.

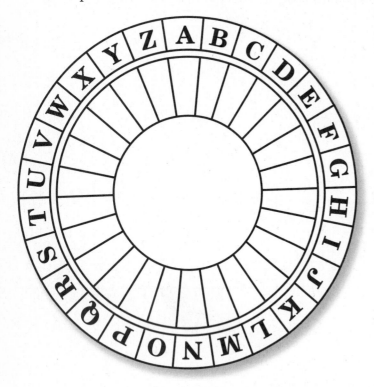

Use the secret code to read this message.

91-2000-1000-300-910   35.9-690-79!

__ __ __ __ __   __ __ __!

Now use the secret code to write a message to a partner in the space below. Exchange papers and decipher the messages.

A	Round 345 to the hundreds place.	N	Round 43.29 to the nearest tenth.
B	Round 78.9 to the nearest whole number.	O	Round 687.5 to the tens place.
C	Round 3.354 to the nearest hundredth.	P	Round 3838 to the thousands place.
D	Round 15.65 to the nearest tenth.	Q	Round 15.33 to the nearest tenth.
E	Round 1092 to the thousands place.	R	Round 2029 to the hundreds place.
F	Round 390.2 to the nearest whole number.	S	Round 120.39 to the hundreds place.
G	Round 90.89 to the nearest whole number.	T	Round 908.7 to the tens place.
H	Round 98.33 to the nearest tenth.	U	Round 555 to the hundreds place.
I	Round 783 to the hundreds place.	V	Round 370.2 to the nearest whole number.
J	Round 35.85 to the nearest tenth.	W	Round 1.453 to the nearest hundredth.
K	Round 3.921 to the nearest hundredth.	X	Round 287.4 to the nearest whole number.
L	Round 195.5 to the nearest whole number.	Y	Round 11.11 to the nearest tenth.
M	Round 38.3 to the tens place.	Z	Round 93 to the tens place.

Parent Activities

1. When shopping at the grocery store or for clothes, have your child round the prices to the nearest whole dollar.

2. Use the Internet, newspaper, or television to find rainfall totals for your area. Then encourage your child to estimate the rainfall to the nearest half-inch (e.g., a total of 1.4 inches would be about 1.5 inches of rain, whereas a total of 2.2 inches would be about 2 inches of rain).

         Level 5

1. Sands Elementary School purchased math workbooks for each student. They purchased 18 boxes of workbooks with 24 workbooks in each box. How many workbooks did the school purchase? Show your work.

   Answer: _____

2. Tessa made an error when multiplying 136 and 18.

$$
\begin{array}{r}
136 \\
\times\ 18 \\
\hline
1088 \\
136\ \ \\
\hline
1224
\end{array}
$$

   What mistake did Tessa make?

   Answer: _____

   _____

3. The Sports Store sells all tennis shoes for $129 per pair. On Saturday they sold 67 pairs. How much money did the store collect? Show your work.

   Answer: _____

4. Rickie and Louis started a pet-sitting service. They charge $6 each day per pet. How much would an owner with 2 pets pay for 7 days of service? Show your work.

   Answer: _____

5. The Buckeye Candy Company packs and ships 3 types of candy. This chart shows the number of cartons of each kind of candy they shipped last month.

   Candy Shipped

Type of Candy	Boxes per Carton	Number of Cartons
Buckeye Melts	24	148
Ooey-Gooey Bars	18	224
Chocolate Tassies	36	112

   For which types of candy were an equal number of boxes shipped?

   Answer: _____

   _____

6. Lindsey drew this area model to solve 346×17.

	300	40	6
10	3000	400	60
7	2100	280	42

   Explain the next step Lindsey should take to find the product.

   Answer: _____

   _____

Words for the Wise

factor   multiply   partial product   product

You've got this down cold!

★ partner practice

1. The food bank has 67 shelving units for canned food. Each unit holds 895 cans that weigh approximately 784 pounds. If all the units are full, how many cans are stored at the food bank?

   Ⓐ 1,746   Ⓒ 59,965

   Ⓑ 52,528   Ⓓ 701,680

2. Cinema 4 Movie Theater has four theaters. The theaters contain different arrangements of seats as shown on this chart.

Theater	Rows	Seats per Row
1	26	18
2	45	15
3	32	16
4	48	12

   Which is a true statement about the theaters?

   Ⓐ The theaters all have the same total number of seats.

   Ⓑ Theater 2 has more seats than the other theaters.

   Ⓒ Theaters 3 and 4 have an equal number of seats.

   Ⓓ All the theaters have more than 500 seats.

3. A robin has a heart rate of 456 beats per minute. How many times will a robin's heart beat in one hour?

   Ⓐ 2,736   Ⓒ 13,680

   Ⓑ 10,944   Ⓓ 27,360

4. Monica flew to Hong Kong. The flight took 19 hours, and the plane traveled at an average speed of 547 miles per hour. How many miles did Monica travel?

   Ⓐ 20,786 miles   Ⓒ 9,893 miles

   Ⓑ 10,393 miles   Ⓓ 5,470 miles

5. Marlo multiplied 387 and 49.

$$\begin{array}{r} 387 \\ \times\ 49 \\ \hline 3483 \\ 15,480 \\ \hline 18,863 \end{array}$$

   What observation could her teacher make about the way Marlo solved the problem?

   Ⓐ Marlo found the correct product.

   Ⓑ Marlo multiplied 387 and 40 incorrectly.

   Ⓒ Marlo did not line up the place values of the two factors correctly.

   Ⓓ Marlo added the partial products incorrectly.

6. Lenora's teacher asked her to explain the way she solved 45×14.

45 × 14
First I broke 14 into 10 + 4.
Then I multiplied 45 × 10 = 450.
I also multiplied 45 × 4 = 180.
Finally I added 450 + 180 = 630.

   What mistake did Lenora make in solving the problem?

   Ⓐ Lenora should not have broken 14 into 10 and 4.

   Ⓑ Lenora did not get the correct product of 45 and 10.

   Ⓒ Lenora should have subtracted 180 from 450.

   Ⓓ Lenora did not make a mistake; her answer is correct.

 Level 5

1. Juan bought a used Ford Mustang from his uncle. Juan paid his uncle $206 each month for 2 years. What was the total amount Juan paid for the car?

   Ⓐ $412

   Ⓑ $1236

   Ⓒ $4944

   Ⓓ $5044

2. The owners of Hardy's Pet Parlor want to build a larger shop. The construction company bases construction costs on the total number of square feet in the building. Mrs. Hardy made a chart to compare the floor dimensions of three different rectangular buildings.

   Building Dimensions

Building	Length (feet)	Width (feet)
1	42	36
2	38	38
3	48	32

   Mrs. Hardy can afford to build a shop that is between 1400 and 1450 square feet. Which building should Mrs. Hardy plan to build?

   Ⓐ building 1

   Ⓑ building 2

   Ⓒ building 3

   Ⓓ either building 2 or building 3

3. There are 450 students at Jones Elementary School. Mrs. Reese wants to give each student 75 sheets of paper. How many sheets of paper does Mrs. Reese need to purchase?

   Ⓐ 33,750

   Ⓑ 29,250

   Ⓒ 9,275

   Ⓓ 3,750

4. Bryce used an area model to solve a multiplication problem.

	400	20	5		
10	4,000	200	50	=	4,250
10	4,000	200	50	=	4,250
10	4,000	200	50	=	4,250
2	800	40	10	=	+ 850
					13,600

   Which of these also shows the problem Bryce was solving?

   Ⓐ $\begin{array}{r} 4{,}250 \\ \times\ \ 3 \\ \hline \end{array}$

   Ⓑ $\begin{array}{r} 850 \\ \times\ 12 \\ \hline \end{array}$

   Ⓒ $\begin{array}{r} 425 \\ \times\ 32 \\ \hline \end{array}$

   Ⓓ $\begin{array}{r} 400 \\ \times\ 25 \\ \hline \end{array}$

5. Jamal went camping with 26 Boy Scouts. He collected 17 bags of pine cones with 24 pine cones per bag. How many pine cones did Jamal collect?

   Ⓐ 67

   Ⓑ 408

   Ⓒ 442

   Ⓓ 624

6. Rahj solved this multiplication problem.

   $$\begin{array}{r} 436 \\ \times\ 29 \\ \hline 3{,}874 \\ +\ 8{,}720 \\ \hline 12{,}594 \end{array}$$

   What mistake did Rahj make?

   Ⓐ Rahj did not make a mistake; his answer is correct.

   Ⓑ Rahj did not line up the place values correctly in the partial products.

   Ⓒ Rahj did not multiply 9 × 436 correctly.

   Ⓓ Rahj did not regroup when adding the partial products.

assessment

1. The principal of Clarkston Elementary ordered 12 cases of snacks and 16 cases of juice for Family Fun Night. There were 248 snacks per case. How many snacks were ordered?

   Ⓐ 276   Ⓒ 2976

   Ⓑ 744   Ⓓ 3968

2. Mr. Miller's class plans to sell chocolate bars to raise money for camp. There are 15 students in Mr. Miller's class. Each student must sell 3 boxes of chocolate bars. Each box contains 25 chocolate bars. How many bars does the class need to sell?

   Ⓐ 1125   Ⓒ 315

   Ⓑ 1025   Ⓓ 75

3. Steven bought 2 dozen eggs. Each egg weighed 145 grams. Which shows a way to find the total mass of the eggs?

   Ⓐ $(145 \times 10) + (145 \times 2)$

   Ⓑ $(145 + 10) \times (145 + 2)$

   Ⓒ $(145 \times 10) + (145 \times 10)$

   Ⓓ $(145 \times 20) + (145 \times 4)$

4. This chart shows the numbers of tickets sold for the Saturday performance of a new Broadway musical.

   Ticket Sales

Seat	Number	Price
Orchestra	115	$75
Mezzanine	170	$60
Balcony	165	$53

   Which of these statements about the ticket sales is true?

   Ⓐ The greatest amount of money came from the sale of orchestra seats.

   Ⓑ More money was made from the sale of orchestra seats than from the sale of mezzanine seats.

   Ⓒ The least amount of money came from the sale of balcony seats.

   Ⓓ More money was made from the sale of balcony seats than from the sale of orchestra seats.

5. The YMCA after-school program sponsored a trip to Andrew's Amusement Park. Twelve adults and 38 children rode to the park in the YMCA bus. The ticket prices for the amusement park are shown on the sign.

   ANDREW'S
   Amusement Park
   Adult $35
   Child $24

   How much was the total cost of admission for the group?

   Answer: _____

Level 5

Analysis/Analyze

1. There are 23 students in Mrs. Byars' class. Each student sold five PTA memberships at $6 each. Mrs. Byars' class won the PTA membership drive contest, and each student received four ice cream coupons and 25 stickers.

   What is the question if the answer is 575? _____

   _____

   What is the question if the answer is 690? _____

   _____

Analysis/Analyze

2. Jeanna is solving multiplication problems. She wants to place numbers in the boxes below to create the problem with the largest possible product. She uses the digits 1, 3, 5, 7, and 9 only once. How can Jeanna arrange the digits in the boxes to get the largest possible product?

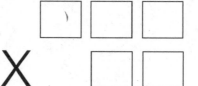

   Explain how you found your answer.

   _____

   _____

   _____

Journal: Analysis/Analyze

Study the problem $1 \times 2 \times 4 \times 8$. You can increase one of the factors by 1. Which one of the four factors will cause the greatest increase in the product when increased by 1? Why do you think this factor caused the greatest increase?

_____

_____

_____

★ motivation station

Hit the Target

Using one game board, play *Hit the Target* with a partner. Each player needs 6 game markers (one color per player). Each pair of players needs 4 number cubes. At the beginning of each round, one player selects a target number from the game board. Player 1 rolls the 4 number cubes, records the digits rolled, and passes the number cubes to player 2 who also rolls and records the four digits. At the teacher's signal, both players use their 4 digits to create two 2-digit numbers to multiply together. The player with the product that comes closest to the target number, without going over, wins the space and places a game marker over the target number. Repeat for each round, alternating which player selects the target number. The winner is the first player to cover 6 target numbers.

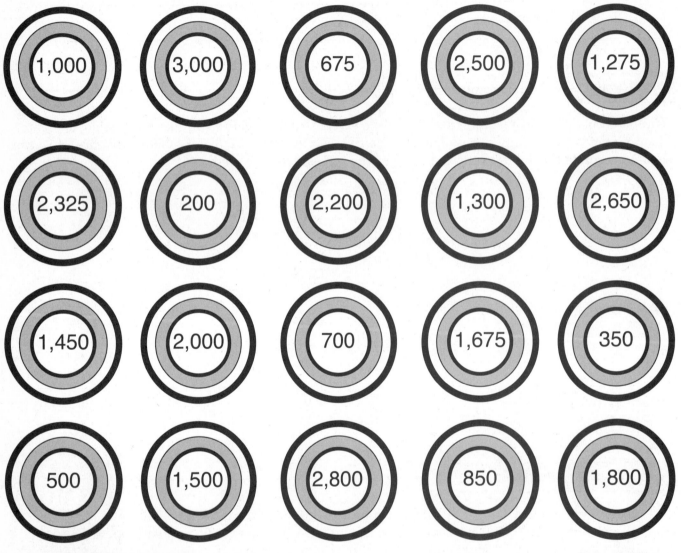

1,000	3,000	675	2,500	1,275
2,325	200	2,200	1,300	2,650
1,450	2,000	700	1,675	350
500	1,500	2,800	850	1,800

Parent Activities

1. Make 2 cards for each number 0–9. Place the cards face down on a table. Have your child turn over 4 cards, make two 2-digit numbers, and find the product (the answer to a multiplication problem).

2. Use dominoes to practice multiplication. Have your child take two dominoes, read each domino as a 2-digit number, and multiply to find the product.

 Level 5

1. Mark's mother prepared 1368 ounces of lemonade for his school dance. This will be enough lemonade to fill 76 cups. All the cups are the same size. How many ounces of lemonade will each cup hold?

   Answer: _____

2. Rodney drew the following area model to find the quotient of 7752 ÷ 38.

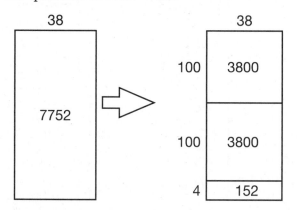

   What quotient did Rodney find?

   Answer: _____

   Explain how Rodney used the model to find the quotient.

   _____

   _____

   _____

3. Wagner's Wholesale Jewelry Store displays charms in trays that hold 49 charms each. The store has 3860 charms to display. How many display trays will be needed?

   Answer: _____

4. Carlos drove 1064 miles on his vacation. He averaged 56 miles per hour. How many total hours did Carlos drive?

   Answer: _____

5. Brinley began to solve this division problem.

$$
\begin{array}{r}
1\square \\
33\overline{)3{,}402} \\
\underline{3\ 3} \\
10
\end{array}
$$

   What digit should Brinley write in the box?

   Answer: _____

   Explain how you found the missing digit.

   _____

   _____

   _____

Words for the Wise

Nothing can stop you now!

digit	divisor
dividend	quotient

remainder

partner practice

1. Juan is unloading 2262 pounds of pine bark mulch from two of his father's trucks. Juan unloads a total of 58 bags. How many pounds does each bag weigh?

Ⓐ 3 lb

Ⓑ 38 lb

Ⓒ 39 lb

Ⓓ 78 lb

2. The members of the reading club each read 34 books in the fall semester and 33 books in the spring semester. Altogether, the club members read 2412 books during the two semesters. How many members are in the reading club?

Ⓐ 36

Ⓑ 37

Ⓒ 38

Ⓓ 71

3. Mr. Arcinega will buy water bottles for the 7175 people who entered the Tri-State 5K Fun Run. The water bottles are packaged 18 per case. What is the least number of cases Mr. Arcinega needs to buy so that each runner can have at least one water bottle?

Ⓐ 380

Ⓑ 398

Ⓒ 399

Ⓓ 400

4. Allyne must divide 9975 by 21 for her math class. Which area model will help her?

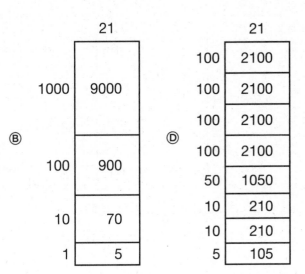

5. Cesar needs to find this quotient.

$$37\overline{)7437}$$

Which shows a strategy Cesar could use?

Ⓐ $7437 \div 37 = (7400 \div 37) \times (37 \div 37)$

Ⓑ $7437 \div 37 = (7400 \div 37) + (37 \div 37)$

Ⓒ $7437 \div 37 = (37 \times 200) \div (37 \times 1)$

Ⓓ $7437 \div 37 = (74 \div 37) + (3 \div 37) + (7 \div 37)$

  Level 5

1. Mrs. Yamo bought 2 boxes of plastic bags. She had 1988 craft sticks. She divided the craft sticks equally among the plastic bags for each of her 28 students. How many sticks did Mrs. Yamo put in each bag?

Ⓐ 26   Ⓒ 71

Ⓑ 35   Ⓓ 72

2. Mrs. Averitt types an average of 62 words per minute. How many minutes does it take her to type 3596 words?

Ⓐ 6 min   Ⓒ 58 min

Ⓑ 57 min   Ⓓ 69 min

3. Mega Mart received 1447 fish. The store's manager put 76 fish into each of the store's aquariums. Then he purchased the remaining 3 fish for his own aquarium. How many aquariums does Mega Mart have?

Ⓐ 18   Ⓒ 20

Ⓑ 19   Ⓓ 22

4. The hens at Colston's Egg Farm laid 9663 eggs last month. Mr. Colston put 4 dozen eggs in each packing crate. How many eggs did Mr. Colston have left after he filled as many crates as possible?

Ⓐ 3   Ⓒ 16

Ⓑ 15   Ⓓ 201

5. Marnie volunteered to help check out books at her city library for 22 days in the summer. During this time, she checked out a total of 4686 books. Marnie made this area model to find the average number of books she checked out each day.

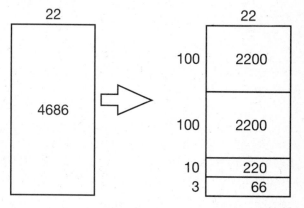

Which is the final step Marnie must complete to solve the problem?

Ⓐ 2200 × 22

Ⓑ 2200 + 2200 + 220 + 66

Ⓒ 220 − 66

Ⓓ 100 + 100 + 10 + 3

6. Martin divided 1250 by 25. His steps are shown.

$$1250 \div 25$$

Step 1: $(1000 + 200 + 50) \div 25$

Step 2: $(1000 \div 25) + (200 \div 25) + (50 \div 25)$

Step 3: $400 + 8 + 2$

Step 4: 482

In which step did Martin make his first mistake?

Ⓐ Step 1   Ⓒ Step 3

Ⓑ Step 2   Ⓓ Step 4

★ assessment

1. Rayville Elementary is sponsoring a math competition for 78 students. During the competition, the students will work a total of 8970 math problems in 4 hours. Each student works the same number of problems. How many problems will each student work?

   Ⓐ 12   Ⓒ 115

   Ⓑ 114   Ⓓ 116

2. Bruce bought 5 packages of notebook paper for a total of 2508 sheets of notebook paper. Bruce uses 12 sheets of notebook paper per day. How many days will the notebook paper last?

   Ⓐ 29   Ⓒ 209

   Ⓑ 200 R9   Ⓓ 290

3. Mr. Vega's archery team raised $6573 selling snacks at an archery meet. This amount will pay the registration fee for 48 students to attend an archery workshop. There will be $45 left to start a savings account for next year's workshop. How much does it cost for one student to attend the archery workshop?

   Ⓐ $71   Ⓒ $137

   Ⓑ $136   Ⓓ $146

4. Jaquita was given this equation to solve.

   $$1739 \div 37 = \boxed{}$$

   She drew an area model to find the quotient.

   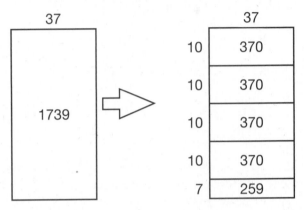

   What should be Jaquita's next step?

   Ⓐ 10 + 10 + 10 + 10 + 7 = 47

   Ⓑ 10 × 10 × 10 × 10 + 7 = 47

   Ⓒ 4 × 10 × 10 + 7 = 407

   Ⓓ 370 + 370 + 370 + 370 + 259 = 1739

5. The Taft School Band visited a water park. The 89 band members spent a total of $4628 at the park. What was the total cost per student to visit the water park?

   Ⓐ $66   Ⓒ $54

   Ⓑ $62   Ⓓ $52

6. Sharonda needs 4368 beads to make necklaces for the school bazaar. Beads are sold in packages of 76. What is the least number of packages of beads Sharonda should purchase to make the necklaces?

   Answer: _____

   Explain how you found your answer.

   _____

   _____

     Level 5

Analysis/Analyze

1. Name three 2-digit numbers that divide into 1520 with a remainder of 8.

   Answer: _____ _____ _____

   Explain how you found your answers.

   _____

   _____

   _____

Synthesis/Create

2. Write a division word problem that can be solved using this area model.

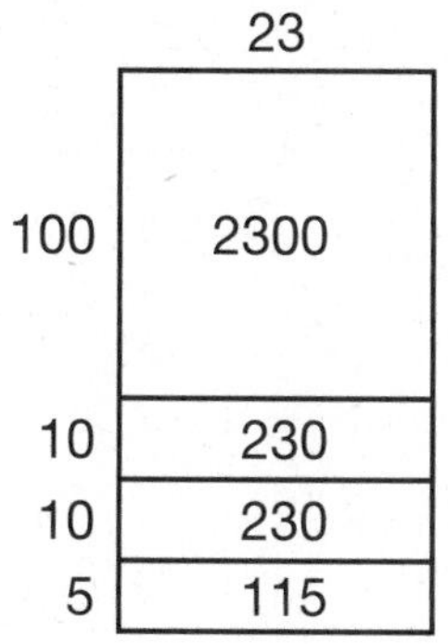

	23
100	2300
10	230
10	230
5	115

   _____

   _____

   _____

   _____

   Explain how your problem can be solved.

   _____

   _____

Journal: Application/Apply

Give an example of a situation in your life when you need to use division. Is the remainder important or not important in your situation? Why or why not?

_____

_____

_____

Division Dilemma

In each division problem below, the letters A, B, and C each represent a different digit.

1. What values for A, B, and C would make this division problem correct?

```
        97 RC
    A6 )AC96
      −ABC
        B56
      −B5B
         C
```

A = _____

B = _____

C = _____

2. What values for A, B, and C would make this division problem correct?

```
         176
    BA ) 7ABA
       −BA
        3AB
      −C8A
        CBA
      −CBA
```

A = _____

B = _____

C = _____

Parent Activities

1. Use a road map to find the distance between 2 locations. Have your child calculate the time it would take to travel if the rate of speed is 60 miles per hour.

2. Together with your child, find a package of food with a price sticker and count the number of individual food items inside the package. Calculate the cost of one item (e.g., 1 slice of bread, 1 slice of cheese, etc.).

1. Scott created a video presentation to show his work on his science project. The first segment of the presentation was 2.1 minutes long, and the second segment was 0.97 minutes long.

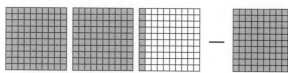

   First Segment   Second Segment

   Write and solve an equation to find how many minutes longer the first segment of Scott's presentation was than the second segment.

   Answer: _____

2. Parker and his family are on vacation in their motor home that travels 3.2 miles on 1 gallon of gasoline. The fuel gauge shows that the motor home has 4.3 gallons of gasoline left in the tank. Parker writes this equation to find how many more miles the motor home can travel before running out of gas.

$$3.2 \times 4.3 = \boxed{}$$

   Use the area model to find the product of Parker's equation.

   3.2
   4.3
   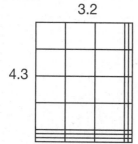

   Answer: _____

3. Annabeth has 7.2 cups of cookie batter, represented by this model.

   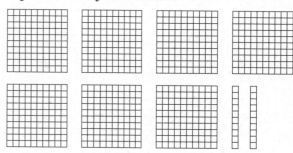

   If each cookie uses 0.45 cup of batter, how many cookies can Annabeth make?

   Answer: _____

4. Hector plans to cut a 10.8-decimeter rope in order to repair the rope ladder on his swing set. How many 2.4-decimeter sections of rope can Hector cut?

   not drawn to scale

   Answer: _____

5. Mr. Pete pumped 18.6 gallons of gasoline into his car and then bought 2.3 gallons of gasoline for his lawn mower. Write an equation to find the number of gallons of gasoline Mr. Pete purchased. Use the number line to solve your equation.

   Answer: _____

Words for the Wise

3 cheers for math!

addend	factor
decimal number	hundredth
decimal point	product
difference	quotient

sum

tenth

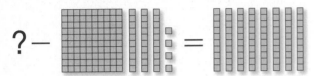
partner practice

1. Four students in Mrs. Johansen's math class solved this equation.

? – 🔲▊▊⋮ = ▊▊▊▊▊▊

The answers are shown here.

Student	Answer
Abby	0.54
Brian	1.14
Carter	1.41
Dennis	2.14

Which student solved the equation correctly?

Ⓐ Abby

Ⓑ Brian

Ⓒ Carter

Ⓓ Dennis

2. Missy bought 4.5 pounds of apples. She used 2.8 pounds of apples to make a pie and the remaining apples to make a fruit salad. How many pounds of apples did Missy use in the fruit salad?

Ⓐ 12.6 lb

Ⓑ 7.3 lb

Ⓒ 2.3 lb

Ⓓ 1.7 lb

3. Which equation does this model show?

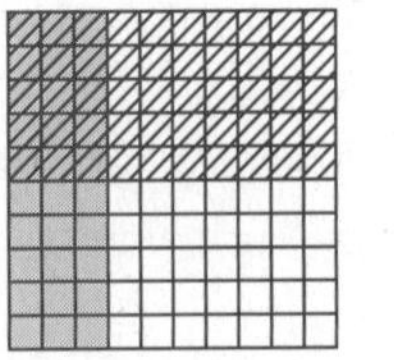

Ⓐ $0.5 \times 0.3 = 0.15$

Ⓑ $0.1 \times 0.7 = 0.07$

Ⓒ $0.5 \times 0.5 = 0.25$

Ⓓ $0.05 \times 0.03 = 0.015$

4. Benita has a strip of paper 6.5 centimeters long. She cuts the paper into 0.5-centimeter sections in order to make tiles for a mosaic. How many tiles does Benita cut?

not drawn to scale

Ⓐ 1.3   Ⓒ 13

Ⓑ 7   Ⓓ 15

5. Stephen and Nathan made a banner for the school play. The banner contains 0.75 meters of white fabric, 1.5 meters of red fabric, and 1.25 meters of blue fabric. Use the number line to show the fabric used for the banner.

Which shows the total length of white, red, and blue fabric used in the banner?

Ⓐ 2.15 m   Ⓒ 3.55 m

Ⓑ 3.5 m   Ⓓ 4 m

1. Hank's rain gauge showed that 2 inches of rain fell on Saturday. On Sunday, Hank checked his rain gauge again and found that 1.4 inches of rain had fallen that day.

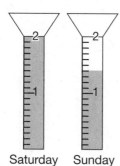

Saturday   Sunday

Choose the equation Hank can use to find how many more inches of rain fell on Saturday than on Sunday.

Ⓐ 2 − 0.4 = 0.6

Ⓑ 2 + 1.4 = 3.4

Ⓒ 2 − 1.4 = 1.2

Ⓓ 2 − 1.4 = 0.6

2. Anna broke a stick of gum into pieces that were 2.8 centimeters long. The stick of gum was long enough to break into 2.5 pieces. How many centimeters long was the original stick of gum?

not drawn to scale

Ⓐ 1.12 cm

Ⓑ 5.3 cm

Ⓒ 7 cm

Ⓓ 70 cm

3. Sue runs a lap around the track in 2.5 minutes. Sue drew this model to help predict how long it would take to run 3.5 laps at the same rate.

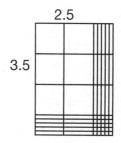

Which shows the number of minutes it will take Sue to run the laps?

Ⓐ 87.5 min   Ⓒ 8.25 min

Ⓑ 8.75 min   Ⓓ 7.0 min

4. Mr. Ponce wants to plant 4.2 acres of peach trees in the field behind his house, as represented on the number line.

If he plants 0.4 acres per day, how many days will it take Mr. Ponce to finish planting the trees?

Ⓐ 1 .05 days   Ⓒ 10.5 days

Ⓑ 10.2 days   Ⓓ 21 days

5. Study the decimal model.

Which of the following is **not** represented by this model?

Ⓐ 0.3 × 0.7 = 0.21   Ⓒ 0.21 ÷ 0.3 = 0.7

Ⓑ 0.21 ÷ 0.7 = 0.3   Ⓓ 0.21 + 0.09 = 0.7

★ assessment

1. Mrs. Ogden's class measured flatworms. The worm Taylor measured was 1.75 inches long, and the worm Mei measured was 1.5 inches long.

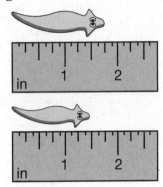

not drawn to scale

Taylor and Mei wrote this equation to find the combined lengths of their worms, in inches.

$$1.75 + 1.5 = \boxed{}$$

What digit is in the tenths place in the sum?

Ⓐ 0   Ⓒ 5

Ⓑ 2   Ⓓ 9

2. Which equation does the decimal model show?

Ⓐ $0.6 \times 0.4 = 2.4$ Ⓒ $0.6 \times 0.4 = 0.24$

Ⓑ $0.4 \times 0.4 = 0.16$ Ⓓ $0.04 \times 0.06 = 0.24$

3. Mr. Sandoval's tractor can travel 1 mile on 1.3 gallons of gasoline. He must drive his tractor 2.2 miles in order to plow his field. The expression 2.2×1.3 represents the number of gallons of gasoline Mr. Sandoval will use to plow his field. Use the area model to find the value of the expression.

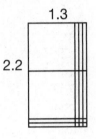

Ⓐ 0.9   Ⓒ 3.5

Ⓑ 2.86   Ⓓ 28.6

4. Reginald listened to the weather report and heard that 6.75 centimeters of rain fell in 4.5 hours. He wants to use this number line to find the average rainfall in one hour.

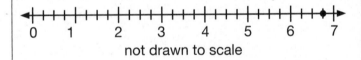

not drawn to scale

Which of the following equations will help Reginald solve his problem?

Ⓐ $6.75 \div 4.5 = 0.15$ Ⓒ $6.75 \div 4.5 = 1.5$

Ⓑ $4.5 \div 6.75 = 0.67$ Ⓓ $6.75 - 4.5 = 2.25$

5. Rosemary has 1.8 pounds of cat food as represented in the model. Her cat eats 0.36 pounds of food each day. Write and solve an equation to find the number of days Rosemary's cat food will last.

Answer: _____

Explain how you found your answer.

_____

_____

_____

Analysis/Analyze

1. Which is greater? Circle your answer.

    4 ÷ 0.5

    Or

    0.5 ÷ 4

    Explain your answer.

    _____

    _____

Synthesis/Create

2. Write a story problem in which the product is 2.4.

    _____

    _____

    _____

    _____

    Draw a picture that models your problem.

Journal: Synthesis/Create

Some students believe that dividing with decimals can be tricky. Write two tips that are helpful when dividing with decimals.

_____

_____

_____

Decimal Goal Line

Play *Decimal Goal Line* with a partner. The object of the game is to move a game token across the other player's goal line. Each pair of players needs a small game token, such as a centimeter cube. Determine who will spin first, then place the game token on the square at 1.5 on the number line.

Player 1 spins the spinner. The number spun tells how many tenths the player may move toward the opponent's goal line. The player states the starting location, the size of the move, and the ending location. For example, "I am starting on 1.6 and moving 0.3. I ended at 1.9." If a player incorrectly states the result of the move, the player remains on the previous location. Play then passes to Player 2 who repeats this process and moves the token in the opposite direction, again stating the starting point, the size of the move, and the ending point. Play continues until the teacher calls time or until one player crosses the other player's goal line.

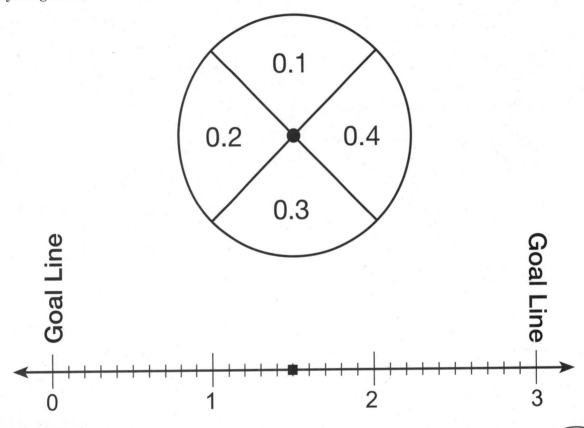

Parent Activities

1. Using a rain gauge, have your child add the rain totals over a period of time, paying close attention to tenths and hundredths.

2. Have your child choose items from a catalog and add the prices to get as close as possible to a total of $5, $10, etc.

3. Give your child several quarters, dimes or nickels. Have your child write the value of each coin as a decimal and multiply the decimal amount by the number of coins to find the total value.

4. Using several quarters, dimes or nickels, calculate the value of the coins, but do not show the coins to your child. Ask a question such as, "I have some quarters. The total value is $2.25. How many quarters do I have?" Your child can solve by dividing the total by the value of one coin.

1. Cade ordered a small cheese pizza at Pizza Time. Yvette ordered a small pepperoni pizza. Cade's pizza was cut into 4 equal slices, and Yvette's pizza was cut into 3 equal slices. The figures are shaded to show the portions of pizza Cade and Yvette ate. Expressed as a fraction, how much more pizza did Cade eat than Yvette?

Cade's Pizza   Yvette's Pizza

Answer: _____

2. Using the steps shown, Gerardo incorrectly answered a problem on his math quiz.

$$\frac{5}{9} = \frac{15}{24}$$

$$+\frac{5}{12} = \frac{10}{24}$$

$$\frac{25}{24} = \frac{11}{24}$$

What was Gerardo's mistake?

Answer: _____

_____

3. Harper picked $3\frac{1}{2}$ baskets of apples. Cooper picked $4\frac{1}{4}$ baskets of apples. How many baskets of apples did Harper and Cooper pick?

Answer: _____

4. Dakota created a volcano model for his science class. The volcano sits on a $7\frac{4}{5}$-pound board. The entire model, including the board, weighs $12\frac{1}{10}$ pounds. How many pounds does Dakota's volcano weigh?

Answer: _____

5. Mrs. Holloway purchased 1 gallon of fruit punch. She poured $\frac{1}{2}$ gallon of punch into cups for her son and his friends as an after-school snack. Mr. Holloway drank $\frac{1}{8}$ gallon of punch after mowing the lawn. What fraction of the gallon of punch was left?

Answer: _____

Words for the Wise

You are brilliant!

common denominator	improper fraction	
denominator	least common denominator	
difference	lowest terms	
equivalent fractions	mixed number	simplify
fraction	numerator	sum

★ partner practice

1. Kalli's pencil box weighs $\frac{1}{3}$ pound, and her notebook weighs $\frac{4}{5}$ pound. What is the total weight, in pounds, of Kalli's pencil box and notebook?

   Ⓐ $\frac{7}{15}$ lb

   Ⓒ $1\frac{2}{15}$ lb

   Ⓑ $\frac{5}{8}$ lb

   Ⓓ $1\frac{7}{15}$ lb

2. Everett is reading a book for his language arts class. He read $\frac{1}{3}$ of the book on Saturday, $\frac{3}{8}$ of the book on Sunday, and $\frac{1}{4}$ of the book on Monday. Which procedure can Everett use to find the total fraction of the book he has read?

   Ⓐ Write equivalent fractions using a common denominator. Then subtract the sum of the fractions from 1.

   Ⓑ Add the numerators of all 3 fractions. Then add the denominators.

   Ⓒ Find the sum of $\frac{1}{3}$ and $\frac{3}{8}$. Then subtract $\frac{1}{4}$.

   Ⓓ Write equivalent fractions using a common denominator. Then find the sum of the fractions.

3. Kevin's kite stayed in the air $6\frac{7}{12}$ minutes on Monday before falling to the ground. This was $2\frac{1}{6}$ minutes longer than the kite stayed in the air on Sunday. How many minutes did Kevin's kite stay in the air on Sunday?

   Ⓐ $4\frac{5}{12}$ min

   Ⓒ $8\frac{5}{12}$ min

   Ⓑ $4\frac{1}{2}$ min

   Ⓓ $8\frac{3}{4}$ min

4. Laney needs $3\frac{4}{7}$ bags of beads to create a mosaic. She needs $\frac{2}{3}$ bag of beads to make jewelry. How many bags of beads does Laney need for her mosaic and jewelry?

   Ⓐ $2\frac{19}{21}$

   Ⓒ $3\frac{16}{21}$

   Ⓑ $3\frac{2}{21}$

   Ⓓ $4\frac{5}{21}$

5. Mr. Brown bought $2\frac{2}{3}$ pounds of bananas and $3\frac{1}{2}$ pounds of apples at the grocery store. How many more pounds of apples than bananas did Mr. Brown purchase?

   Ⓐ $\frac{1}{6}$ lb

   Ⓒ $1\frac{1}{6}$ lb

   Ⓑ $\frac{5}{6}$ lb

   Ⓓ $1\frac{1}{2}$ lb

6. Look at this number line.

   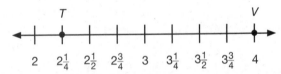

   Which of the following represents the distance between point T and point V?

   Ⓐ $2\frac{19}{21}$

   Ⓒ $1\frac{1}{2}$

   Ⓑ $1\frac{3}{4}$

   Ⓓ $1\frac{1}{4}$

 Level 5

1. Ms. Arnold and Ms. Bradshaw each baked a pie for a meeting at work. Although the pies were the same size, Ms. Arnold's pie was cut into 8 equal slices and Ms. Bradshaw's pie was cut into 6 equal slices. The figures are shaded to show the portions of each pie that were not eaten. Expressed as a fraction, how much more of Ms. Arnold's pie was eaten than Ms. Bradshaw's pie?

Ms. Arnold   Ms. Bradshaw

Ⓐ $\frac{1}{8}$ Ⓒ $\frac{1}{4}$

Ⓑ $\frac{5}{24}$ Ⓓ $\frac{11}{24}$

2. Rob incorrectly solved a problem using these steps.

$$\frac{5}{6} = \frac{25}{30}$$

$$+\frac{3}{10} = \frac{3}{30}$$

$$\frac{28}{30} = \frac{14}{15}$$

What was Rob's first mistake?

Ⓐ The common denominator should be 60 instead of 30.

Ⓑ He wrote the wrong equivalent fraction for $\frac{5}{6}$.

Ⓒ He wrote the wrong equivalent fraction for $\frac{3}{10}$.

Ⓓ He simplified the answer incorrectly.

3. The snowfall between midnight and 6 a.m. was $3\frac{3}{4}$ feet. The snowfall between 6 a.m. and noon was $2\frac{1}{3}$ feet. How many more feet of snow fell during the first six hours of the day than during the second six hours of the day?

Ⓐ $\frac{5}{12}$ ft   Ⓒ $1\frac{2}{3}$ ft

Ⓑ $1\frac{5}{12}$ ft   Ⓓ $5\frac{4}{7}$ ft

4. Gomez prepares hot chocolate mix using this recipe.

> **Hot Chocolate Mix**
>
> Ingredients:
>
> $11\frac{1}{4}$ cups dry powdered milk
>
> $\frac{3}{4}$ cup non-dairy creamer
>
> $2\frac{1}{2}$ cups powdered sugar
>
> $2\frac{1}{3}$ cups instant chocolate drink mix

When all ingredients are mixed together, how many cups of hot chocolate mix will Gomez have?

Ⓐ $15\frac{6}{13}$ cups   Ⓒ $16\frac{1}{12}$ cups

Ⓑ $15\frac{6}{8}$ cups   Ⓓ $16\frac{5}{6}$ cups

5. Brittney's hair was $17\frac{3}{8}$ inches long. After a haircut, her hair was $12\frac{5}{6}$ inches long. How many inches were cut?

Ⓐ $4\frac{13}{24}$ in   Ⓒ $5\frac{13}{24}$ in

Ⓑ $4\frac{11}{24}$ in   Ⓓ $5\frac{11}{24}$ in

assessment

1. Nandry rode her bike $\frac{7}{10}$ mile from her house to her aunt's house. On the way home, her bike had a flat tire $\frac{1}{4}$ mile from her aunt's house. What fractional part of a mile must Nandry walk to get home?

   Ⓐ $\frac{8}{40}$ mi   Ⓒ $\frac{8}{14}$ mi

   Ⓑ $\frac{9}{20}$ mi   Ⓓ $\frac{19}{20}$ mi

2. Shelly and Marcom are selling popcorn for their music club. Each received a case of popcorn to sell. Shelly sold $\frac{7}{8}$ of her case, and Marcom sold $\frac{5}{6}$ of his case. Which of the following explains how to find the portion of popcorn they sold together?

   Ⓐ Add the numerators and denominators of the fractions.

   Ⓑ Subtract the numerators and denominators of the fractions.

   Ⓒ Find the common denominator for the fractions, and use it to write equivalent fractions. Then add the fractions.

   Ⓓ Find the common denominator for the fractions, and use it to write equivalent fractions. Then subtract the fractions.

3. Tonya watched videos for $\frac{2}{3}$ hour, played checkers for $\frac{3}{4}$ hour, and practiced soccer for $1\frac{1}{6}$ hours. How many hours did Tonya spend on these three activities?

   Ⓐ $1\frac{5}{6}$ hr   Ⓒ $2\frac{7}{12}$ hr

   Ⓑ $1\frac{7}{12}$ hr   Ⓓ $2\frac{5}{6}$ hr

4. Farmer Brown has a 75-acre farm. He planted $5\frac{7}{8}$ acres in corn and $4\frac{2}{3}$ acres in wheat. He used the rest as grazing land. How many more acres did Farmer Brown plant in corn than wheat?

   Ⓐ $\frac{5}{24}$ acre   Ⓒ $10\frac{13}{24}$ acres

   Ⓑ $1\frac{5}{24}$ acres   Ⓓ $70\frac{13}{24}$ acres

5. Andres had a photo 5 inches long and $3\frac{1}{2}$ inches wide, as shown in Figure 1. He used scissors to crop his photo, as shown in Figure 2, so that it would fit into his scrapbook.

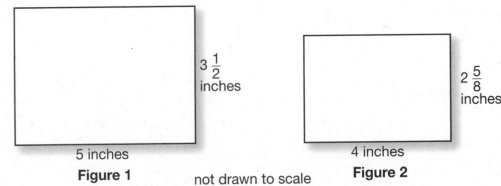

Figure 1   not drawn to scale   Figure 2

How many inches did Andres cut off the width of his photo?

Answer: _____

Name _____

Application/Apply

1. Yamir was given several chores to complete on Saturday. He began working at noon. Yamir created this table to show the fractional part of an hour he spent completing each chore.

Chore	Time Spent (hours)
Feeding dog	$\frac{1}{12}$
Cleaning room	$\frac{3}{4}$
Drying dishes	$\frac{1}{3}$
Hanging up clothes	$\frac{1}{6}$

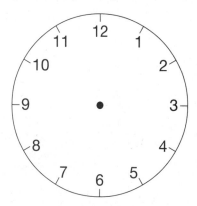

Yamir looked at a clock when his chores were finished. Use the blank clock face to draw the time he saw.

Explain your answer. _____

_____

_____

Analysis/Analyze

2. Brendan wrote this sequence of numbers.

$$12, \ 11\frac{1}{3}, \ 10\frac{2}{3}, \ 10, \ 9\frac{1}{3}$$

Ella wrote this sequence of numbers.

$$1\frac{1}{2}, \ 3, \ 4\frac{1}{2}, \ 6, \ 7\frac{1}{2}, \ 9$$

What is the sum of the ninth terms of Brendan's and Ella's sequences?   **Answer:** _____

Explain your answer. _____

_____

Journal: Analysis/Analyze

Name a profession in which mixed numbers are used in everyday situations. Give examples of how mixed numbers are used in this profession.

_____

_____

_____

Don't Let Fractions Bug You

Play *Don't Let Fractions Bug You* with the whole class. Each player needs a pencil or crayon and the game board. The teacher signals "start" to begin the game. Players solve the fraction problems and color the ladybug spots that match the answers. The winner is the first person to color all the ladybug spots.

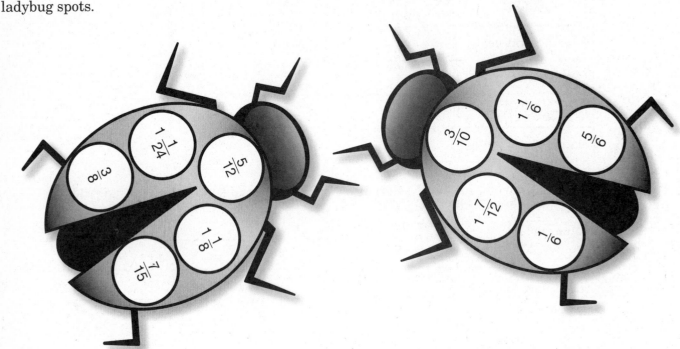

Fraction Problems	
$\frac{2}{3} + \frac{3}{6}$	$\frac{2}{4} + \frac{5}{8}$
$\frac{9}{12} - \frac{1}{3}$	$\frac{2}{6} + \frac{1}{2}$
$\frac{4}{6} - \frac{1}{2}$	$\frac{4}{5} - \frac{1}{3}$
$\frac{1}{2} - \frac{1}{8}$	$\frac{1}{2} - \frac{2}{10}$
$\frac{3}{4} + \frac{5}{6}$	$\frac{5}{8} + \frac{5}{12}$

Parent Activities

1. Give your child $10\frac{1}{2}$ minutes to complete an activity such as drying dishes. Then interrupt your child partway through the task with a question such as, "You have been working for $5\frac{3}{4}$ minutes. How much time do you have left to work?" Encourage your child to subtract the mixed numbers to find the solution.

2. Let your child pour water into measuring cups to solve fraction addition problems. Add $\frac{1}{2}$ cup and $\frac{1}{4}$ cup to equal $\frac{3}{4}$ cup. Add $\frac{3}{8}$ cup and $\frac{3}{8}$ cup to equal $\frac{3}{4}$ cup.

 Level 5

1. Missy divided her scrapbook page into sections to be decorated. Each section she decorated was either $\frac{1}{6}$ or $\frac{1}{2}$ of the page. The shaded parts of the figure show the sections Missy decorated.

What fractional part of the page did Missy decorate?

Answer: _____

2. Tanya is baking a birthday cake for her mom. The recipe requires $\frac{3}{8}$ stick of butter for the cake and another $\frac{1}{4}$ stick of butter for the frosting. Shade the stick of butter to show the total amount of butter Tanya needs for her cake and frosting.

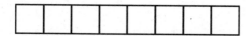

What fraction does your drawing represent?

Answer: _____

3. Hannah grew a total of $\frac{7}{8}$ inch last year. She grew $\frac{3}{4}$ inch between January 1 and June 30 of last year. Write and solve an equation to find the fraction of an inch Hannah grew between July 1 and December 31.

Answer: _____

4. Gary completed $\frac{2}{5}$ of his research paper last week and $\frac{1}{3}$ of his research paper this week. He will finish the paper next week. What fractional part of the paper must Gary complete next week?

Answer: _____

Explain how you found your answer.

_____

_____

_____

5. Megan recorded a television show that lasted $\frac{11}{12}$ hour. When Megan watched the show, she skipped the commercials and saved about $\frac{3}{10}$ hour. Estimate the fractional part of an hour Megan spent watching the recorded show.

Answer: _____

Explain how you found your estimate.

_____

_____

_____

Words for the Wise

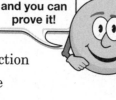

Math matters and you can prove it!

common denominator	fraction	proper fraction
denominator	least common denominator	reasonable
estimate	numerator	unit fraction

partner practice

1. Abigail and Kim made brownies to use as a demonstration for fractional parts. After baking and cutting the brownies, Kim ate $\frac{1}{6}$ of the brownies and Abigail ate $\frac{1}{8}$. Which picture is shaded to show the fraction of the brownies left for their demonstration?

Ⓐ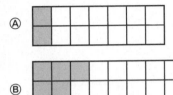

Ⓑ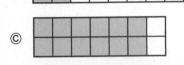

Ⓒ

Ⓓ

2. Marcellus had a pitcher containing $\frac{5}{8}$ gallon of limeade.

Marcellus drank $\frac{1}{4}$ gallon of the limeade, and Marcy drank $\frac{1}{8}$ gallon. What fractional part of a gallon of limeade remained in the pitcher?

Ⓐ $\frac{1}{4}$ gal   Ⓒ $\frac{1}{2}$ gal

Ⓑ $\frac{3}{8}$ gal   Ⓓ $\frac{5}{8}$ gal

3. Cindy put $\frac{2}{3}$ cup of peanuts into a bag for lunch. Then she decided to put another $\frac{1}{5}$ cup of peanuts into the bag. The equation represents the fraction of a cup of peanuts in Cindy's bag.

$$\frac{2}{3} + \frac{1}{5} = \boxed{}$$

What is the sum of the equation?

Ⓐ $\frac{3}{8}$ cup   Ⓒ $\frac{7}{15}$ cup

Ⓑ $\frac{13}{30}$ cup   Ⓓ $\frac{13}{15}$ cup

4. Malcolm needs $\frac{1}{4}$ bag of fertilizer for his lawn. He has $\frac{11}{12}$ bag of fertilizer in his garage. After Malcolm fertilizes his lawn, what fractional part of a bag of fertilizer will be left?

Ⓐ $\frac{1}{2}$ Ⓒ $\frac{3}{4}$

Ⓑ $\frac{2}{3}$ Ⓓ $\frac{10}{12}$

5. Miguel fed his pet rabbits $\frac{5}{6}$ cup of food on Tuesday. He estimated that the rabbits left about $\frac{1}{10}$ cup of food uneaten. Which is a reasonable estimate of the fraction of a cup of food Miguel's rabbits ate on Tuesday?

Ⓐ It is greater than 0 but less than $\frac{1}{4}$.

Ⓑ It is greater than $\frac{1}{4}$ but less than $\frac{1}{3}$.

Ⓒ It is greater than $\frac{1}{3}$ but less than $\frac{1}{2}$.

Ⓓ It is greater than $\frac{1}{2}$ but less than 1.

1. Robert is cutting strips from a foot-long piece of wood for his woodworking class. He needs a strip of wood that is $\frac{3}{8}$ foot long and another strip that is $\frac{1}{2}$ foot long. Which of the following strips is shaded to show the total amount of wood Robert needs for his class?

Ⓐ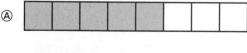

Ⓑ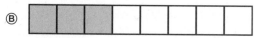

Ⓒ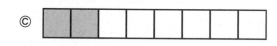

Ⓓ

2. Erin plotted two points on this number line for math class.

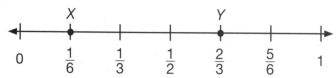

Erin must find the distance between the points. Which of the following represents the distance between point X and point Y?

Ⓐ $\frac{1}{6}$

Ⓑ $\frac{1}{3}$

Ⓒ $\frac{1}{2}$

Ⓓ $\frac{2}{3}$

3. Carly bought 1 dozen eggs. She used $\frac{1}{2}$ dozen eggs when cooking breakfast and $\frac{1}{3}$ dozen eggs to make a cake. What fraction of the dozen eggs does Carly have left?

Ⓐ $\frac{1}{6}$　　　　Ⓒ $\frac{2}{5}$

Ⓑ $\frac{4}{12}$　　　　Ⓓ $\frac{5}{6}$

4. Sergei had $\frac{5}{6}$ pound of gummy bears. He gave $\frac{2}{5}$ pound of gummy bears to Nancy and kept the rest for himself. Sergei wrote this equation to find the fraction of a pound of gummy bears he kept for himself.

$$\frac{5}{6} - \frac{2}{5} = \boxed{}$$

What is the missing number in the equation?

Ⓐ 1 lb　　　　Ⓒ $\frac{7}{11}$ lb

Ⓑ $\frac{23}{30}$ lb　　　　Ⓓ $\frac{13}{30}$ lb

5. Cameron's mom told him he could spend $\frac{11}{12}$ hour playing football before dinner. So far, he has spent $\frac{1}{4}$ hour playing football. Which is a correct estimate of the fractional part of an hour Cameron has left to play football before dinner?

Ⓐ It is greater than 0 but less than $\frac{1}{4}$.

Ⓑ It is greater than $\frac{1}{4}$ but less than $\frac{1}{2}$.

Ⓒ It is greater than $\frac{1}{2}$ but less than $\frac{3}{4}$.

Ⓓ It is greater than $\frac{3}{4}$ but less than 1.

★ assessment

1. Kate, Henry, and Martin each purchased birthday presents for their grandmother. It took $\frac{1}{4}$ yard of giftwrap paper to wrap Henry's present, $\frac{1}{6}$ yard of paper to wrap Kate's present, and $\frac{1}{2}$ yard of paper to wrap Martin's present. Each of these strips represents 1 yard of wrapping paper. Which strip is shaded to represent the amount of paper needed to wrap all three presents?

Ⓐ

Ⓑ

Ⓒ

Ⓓ

2. Enrique has a coin collection. In his collection, $\frac{3}{5}$ of the coins were given to him by his Aunt Rosa, and $\frac{1}{4}$ of the coins were given to him by his parents. Enrique purchased the rest of the coins himself. What fraction of his coin collection did Enrique purchase?

Ⓐ $\frac{3}{20}$　　　Ⓒ $\frac{2}{5}$

Ⓑ $\frac{7}{20}$　　　Ⓓ $\frac{17}{20}$

3. Alexandra is baking cupcakes. She needs $\frac{3}{4}$ cup of sugar to make chocolate cupcakes and $\frac{1}{3}$ cup of sugar to make vanilla cupcakes. Alexandra uses this number line to represent the amounts of sugar she needs for each recipe.

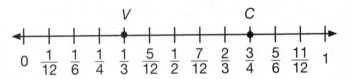

The distance between point V and point C on the number line represents the difference in the amounts of sugar needed for the cupcakes. How much more sugar is needed for the chocolate cupcakes than for the vanilla cupcakes?

Ⓐ $\frac{1}{3}$ cup　　　Ⓒ $\frac{1}{2}$ cup

Ⓑ $\frac{5}{12}$ cup　　　Ⓓ $\frac{5}{6}$ cup

4. Pete took his dog for a walk. Pete's dog walked for about $\frac{1}{4}$ mile and ran for about $\frac{3}{8}$ mile. Which is a correct estimate of the fractional part of a mile Pete's dog walked and ran?

Ⓐ It is greater than 0 but less than $\frac{3}{10}$.

Ⓑ It is greater than $\frac{3}{10}$ but less than $\frac{1}{2}$.

Ⓒ It is greater than $\frac{1}{2}$ but less than $\frac{3}{4}$.

Ⓓ It is greater than $\frac{3}{4}$ but less than 1.

5. Nayati used $\frac{9}{10}$ gallon of water to fill a pool for her little sister's doll. After Nayati's sister played with her doll in the pool, only $\frac{2}{3}$ gallon of water remained in the pool. Write and solve an equation to find the fraction of a gallon of water that splashed out of the pool.

Answer: _____

　　　　　　Level 5

Analysis/Analyze

1. Cecil has this list of fractions.

$$\frac{11}{12} \qquad \frac{5}{12} \qquad \frac{1}{6} \qquad \frac{1}{3} \qquad \frac{17}{24} \qquad \frac{5}{24} \qquad \frac{9}{24} \qquad \frac{3}{4} \qquad \frac{11}{24} \qquad \frac{1}{8}$$

He needs to place the fractions into the Venn diagram. Help Cecil by writing the fractions from the list in the correct area of the diagram.

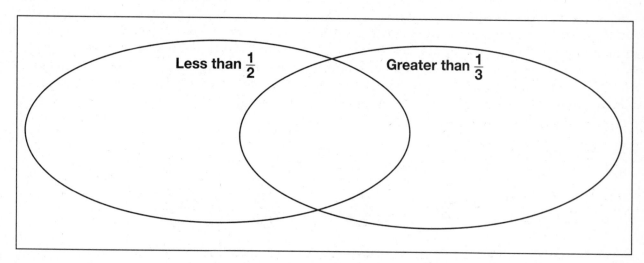

Less than $\frac{1}{2}$ Greater than $\frac{1}{3}$

Synthesis/Create

2. Marni has the number tiles shown here. She uses four different tiles to create two proper fractions. She wants her fractions to have the greatest possible sum. How could Marni arrange the tiles?

2 3 4 5 6 7 $\frac{\Box}{\Box} + \frac{\Box}{\Box} =$

Explain your thinking. _____

_____

_____

Journal: Analysis/Analyze

Luisa was trying to subtract $\frac{1}{8}$ from $\frac{3}{4}$. Her teacher told her to get a standard inch ruler. How could the ruler help Luisa?

_____

_____

_____

★ motivation station

Common Ground

Play *Common Ground* with a partner. Each player needs a different color of crayon or marker. Each pair of players needs one game sheet and two number/dot cubes. Player 1 rolls the number/dot cubes to generate two denominators of unit fractions. For example, if the player rolls 3 and 5, the fractions would be $\frac{1}{3}$ and $\frac{1}{5}$.

The player looks at the game board and selects a number that could be used as a common denominator for the two fractions. For the fractions generated, the player states the equivalent fractions using the selected common denominator. If the equivalent fractions are correct, the player claims the square by shading it with his/her crayon or marker. If the player's equivalent fractions are incorrect, the player loses that turn. Note that the common denominator does not have to be the least common denominator in this game. Play then passes to Player 2. The number 1 is a "wild card." If a 1 is rolled, the player selects any number from 2-6 as a denominator. Play continues until all squares on the board are shaded. The player with the most shaded squares is the winner.

4	6	8	9
10	12	15	16
18	20	24	30

Parent Activities

1. Practice adding halves, fourths, eighths, and sixteenths on a standard inch ruler. Your child could add $\frac{1}{8}$ to $\frac{5}{8}$ and show that the result is $\frac{3}{4}$. Add $\frac{3}{16}$ to $\frac{1}{2}$ and show that the result is $\frac{11}{16}$, etc.

2. Ask your child questions such as, "Would you rather have $\frac{2}{4}$ or $\frac{2}{3}$ hour of homework?" Have your child explain the choice.

3. Discuss professions in which fractions with different denominators are added or subtracted (e.g., carpenter, seamstress, chef, etc.).

Name _____

1. Eight members of the science club equally shared 3 pizzas. What part of a pizza did each member receive?

   Answer: _____

   Draw a picture to represent your answer.

2. Taylor mows lawns every day in June except Sundays. He needs to mow 21 lawns this week and plans to mow the same number of lawns each day. How many lawns does Taylor need to mow each day? Express the quotient as a mixed number.

   Answer: _____

   Between what two whole numbers does your answer lie?

   Answer: _____

3. A group of one dozen teachers shared 7 ounces of chocolate equally. How many ounces of chocolate did each teacher receive?

   Answer: _____

4. During a science investigation, six students divided 15 pounds of potting soil equally. Write an equation that shows how many pounds of potting soil each student received.

   Answer: _____

   Between which two whole numbers does your answer lie?

   Answer: _____

5. The dance teacher is making bows for her students' costumes. She has 24 yards of ribbon and cuts the ribbon into 36 equal pieces. How long, in yards, is each piece of ribbon?

   Answer: _____

6. Logan split a rope that was 28 inches long into 5 equal parts. Leroy split a rope that was 30 inches long into 6 equal parts. Which boy's rope was cut into longer pieces?

   Answer: _____

   Explain your answer.

   _____

   _____

   _____

Words for the Wise

denominator	improper fraction	
division	mixed number	
equation	numerator	
fraction	quotient	whole number

You're on target!

partner practice

1. Five brothers equally shared 3 boxes of snack crackers. What fraction of a box did each brother receive?

   Ⓐ $\frac{1}{2}$ box   Ⓒ $1\frac{1}{2}$ boxes

   Ⓑ $\frac{3}{5}$ box   Ⓓ $\frac{5}{3}$ boxes

2. Margaret has 80 yards of fabric to make costumes for the school play. She needs to make 25 costumes with the fabric and will divide all the fabric equally among the costumes. This equation represents the number of yards of fabric for each costume.

   $$80 \div 25 = \boxed{}$$

   What number correctly completes the equation?

   Ⓐ $3\frac{1}{25}$ yd   Ⓒ $3\frac{1}{2}$ yd

   Ⓑ $3\frac{1}{5}$ yd   Ⓓ $5\frac{3}{25}$ yd

3. A 50-minute block of computer time must be shared equally among Mary and 2 other students in Mrs. Moore's class. Which equation **best** represents Mary's computer time in minutes?

   Ⓐ $\frac{3}{50} = 16\frac{2}{3}$ Ⓒ $\frac{50}{3} = 16\frac{2}{50}$

   Ⓑ $\frac{50}{3} = 16.2$ Ⓓ $\frac{50}{3} = 16\frac{2}{3}$

4. Jim has a box of 9 granola bars to share among the 4 children in his family. He wants to make sure that each child receives exactly the same number of granola bars. Jim first gives each person 2 granola bars. What should he do next?

   Ⓐ Divide 1 bar into 4 equal pieces, so that each person receives a total of $2\frac{1}{4}$ granola bars.

   Ⓑ Divide 1 bar into 2 equal pieces, so that each person receives a total of $2\frac{1}{2}$ granola bars.

   Ⓒ Divide 9 bars into 2 equal pieces, so that each person receives a total of $4\frac{1}{2}$ granola bars.

   Ⓓ Divide 9 bars into 8 equal pieces, so that each person receives a total of $1\frac{1}{8}$ granola bars.

5. Three groups of students are completing a science investigation. The teacher has 5 bags of colored centimeter cubes to share equally among the groups as shown in this diagram.

Group 1	Group 2	Group 3	1	2	3	1	2	3
Bag 1	Bag 2	Bag 3		Bag 4			Bag 5	

   How many bags will each group receive?

   Ⓐ $3\frac{1}{2}$ bags

   Ⓑ $2\frac{1}{3}$ bags

   Ⓒ $1\frac{2}{3}$ bags

   Ⓓ $\frac{3}{5}$ bag

                   Level 5

1. Roseanne purchased 3 dozen boxes of paper clips for her office. She divided the paper clips equally among 5 containers. Which shows the number of boxes of paper clips in each container?

Ⓐ between 0 and 1

Ⓑ between 1 and 2

Ⓒ between 6 and 7

Ⓓ between 7 and 8

2. Dolly's mom told her to share time playing video games equally with her brother and sister. They are allowed a total of 2 hours playing time. How much playing time will each child receive?

Ⓐ $\frac{1}{2}$ hr

Ⓒ $1\frac{1}{4}$ hr

Ⓑ $\frac{2}{3}$ hr

Ⓓ $1\frac{1}{2}$ hr

3. Jane and Joe's mom fixes sausage links for breakfast. There are 7 links to be shared equally between the children. Which equation shows how Jane and Joe can determine the number of sausage links they each receive?

Ⓐ $2 \div 7 = \frac{2}{7}$

Ⓑ $2 \div 7 = 3\frac{1}{2}$

Ⓒ $7 \div 2 = 3\frac{1}{7}$

Ⓓ $7 \div 2 = 3\frac{1}{2}$

4. Mrs. Hall is making sack lunches for the 15 children in her scout group. She has 6 bags of chips to divide equally among the lunches. Which shows the fractional part of a bag of chips that should go in each lunch?

Ⓐ $\frac{1}{15}$

Ⓒ $\frac{2}{5}$

Ⓑ $\frac{1}{6}$

Ⓓ $\frac{15}{6}$

5. Rue has 7 sheets of stickers to share among the 5 children in her family. She wants to make sure that each child receives exactly the same number of stickers. First, Rue gives each child 1 sheet of stickers. What should she do next?

Ⓐ Divide 2 sheets into 2 equal pieces, so that each person receives $2\frac{2}{5}$ sheets of stickers.

Ⓑ Divide 2 sheets into 5 equal pieces, so that each person receives $1\frac{2}{5}$ sheets of stickers.

Ⓒ Divide 7 sheets into 2 equal pieces, so that each person receives $3\frac{1}{2}$ sheets of stickers.

Ⓓ Divide 5 sheets into 7 equal pieces, so that each person receives $\frac{5}{7}$ sheet of stickers.

6. A group of 6 third graders read a total of 29 books. A group of 8 fourth graders read a total of 33 books. Which group won the prize for reading the most books per person?

Ⓐ The third graders won because $4\frac{5}{6}$ is greater than $4\frac{1}{8}$.

Ⓑ The fourth graders won because $4\frac{1}{8}$ is greater than $4\frac{5}{6}$.

Ⓒ The fourth graders won because 33 is greater than 29.

Ⓓ The teams tied because they each read $4\frac{1}{2}$ books per person.

★ assessment

1. Ms. Ligon collected 38 boxes of markers for Hobart Middle School. There are 5 art classes on campus. How many boxes should each class receive if the boxes are divided equally?

   Ⓐ $\frac{5}{38}$ box

   Ⓑ $3\frac{5}{7}$ boxes

   Ⓒ $5\frac{3}{7}$ boxes

   Ⓓ $7\frac{3}{5}$ boxes

2. The school secretary orders 4 dozen boxes of pens. There are 7 fifth-grade classes that will equally share the pens. The number of boxes each class will receive lies between which two whole numbers?

   Ⓐ between 0 and 1 box

   Ⓑ between 1 and 2 boxes

   Ⓒ between 6 and 7 boxes

   Ⓓ between 7 and 8 boxes

3. Eighteen students each made a volcano model for their science class. They used a total of 99 cups of flour. How many cups of flour were used for each volcano if all students used the same amount?

   Ⓐ $4\frac{9}{18}$ cups

   Ⓑ $5\frac{8}{19}$ cups

   Ⓒ $5\frac{1}{3}$ cups

   Ⓓ $5\frac{1}{2}$ cups

4. The 5 members of the Arnold family calculated the family's daily water use as 38 gallons. Which equation shows w, the amount of water each person uses daily?

   Ⓐ $w = \frac{5}{38}$

   Ⓑ $w = \frac{38}{5}$

   Ⓒ $38 = \frac{w}{5}$

   Ⓓ $5 = \frac{w}{38}$

5. Monica's service club is sending cards to children in the hospital. There are 5 members in the club, and they share 9 books of postage stamps. Monica wants to make sure that each member receives exactly the same number of stamps. She gives each member 1 book of stamps. What should Monica do next?

   Ⓐ Divide 4 books into 5 equal parts so that each member receives $1\frac{4}{5}$ books.

   Ⓑ Divide 5 books into 9 equal parts so that each member receives $1\frac{5}{9}$ books.

   Ⓒ Divide 1 book into 5 equal parts so that each member receives $1\frac{1}{5}$ books.

   Ⓓ Divide 4 books into 10 equal parts so that each member receives $1\frac{4}{10}$ books.

6. Micah and 3 friends went fishing on Saturday. Micah caught 9 fish, Sara caught 4 fish, Diego caught 6 fish, and Emily caught 7 fish. Since all the fish were the same size, the group decided to share them equally. How many fish did each person take home?

   Answer: _____

   Draw a model to illustrate the solution.

     Level 5

Analysis/Analyze

1. Find the quotient for both word problems.

   A. Mrs. Tanner has a piece of yarn that is 78 inches long. She wants to cut it into 8 equal segments for a craft project. How many inches long is each segment?

   B. There are 188 students and teachers going on a field trip to the museum. The principal plans for each bus to carry about 40 students. How many buses are needed for the field trip?

   Which quotient is best expressed as a mixed number? _____

   For which problem is a mixed number **not** a reasonable answer? _____

   Explain your thinking. _____

   _____

   _____

Synthesis/Create

2. Using whole numbers, write a division word problem that has a quotient of $\frac{2}{3}$.

   Answer: _____

   _____

   _____

Journal: Analysis/Analyze

How are fractions related to division?

_____

_____

_____

★ **motivation station**

Sketch and Solve

Read each problem on the left page of the notebook. Sketch a model to illustrate each problem on the right page of the notebook. Record each solution on the line below the notebook.

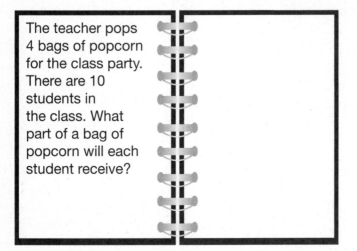

The teacher pops 4 bags of popcorn for the class party. There are 10 students in the class. What part of a bag of popcorn will each student receive?

_____

A family of 6 orders 3 pizzas. If each family member eats an equal amount of pizza, how much will each person eat?

_____

Kinsler has 17 packs of baseball cards. He wants to give an equal number of cards to four friends. How many packs will each friend receive?

_____

School ends in 20 minutes. Three girls want to use the computer but must share the time equally. How many minutes can each girl spend on the computer?

_____

Parent Activities

1. Give your child a handful of cereal or small candies. Have him/her divide the handful into 3 groups, expressing the answer as a mixed number. Have him/her gather the items again and divide into 4, 5, and 6 equal groups.

2. Line up 7 sticks of gum, end to end. Ask your child how many sticks each person in the family would receive if the gum is shared equally (e.g., In a family of 5, each member would receive one whole stick of gum, with 2 sticks remaining. After splitting the two extra sticks, everyone would get $1\frac{2}{5}$ sticks of gum.).

Name _____

1. This model shows $\frac{1}{5}$ shaded. Use the model to show $\frac{1}{2} \times \frac{1}{5}$.

What is the product of $\frac{1}{2} \times \frac{1}{5}$?

Answer: _____

2. The rectangular rug in Jody's room is $8\frac{1}{2}$ feet long and $5\frac{1}{2}$ feet wide. Jody used this diagram to find the area of the rug.

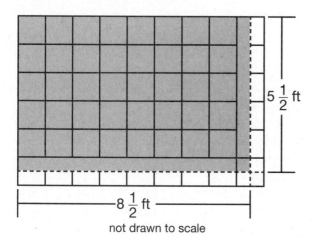

$5\frac{1}{2}$ ft

$8\frac{1}{2}$ ft

not drawn to scale

What is the area of Jody's rug in square feet?

Answer: _____

3. Each day, Maurice walked his dog $1\frac{1}{4}$ miles. How many miles did Maurice walk his dog in 7 days?

Answer: _____

4. Crissy bought 5 bags of candy from the Sugar Shack. Each bag weighed $\frac{5}{6}$ pound.

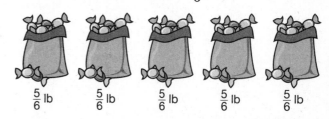

$\frac{5}{6}$ lb $\frac{5}{6}$ lb $\frac{5}{6}$ lb $\frac{5}{6}$ lb $\frac{5}{6}$ lb

Write and solve a multiplication equation to find how many pounds of candy Crissy bought.

Answer: _____

5. Jonas, Frieda, and Rami will spend 10 hours at an amusement park on Saturday. They estimate that $\frac{2}{5}$ of that time will be spent waiting in line. The children decided to calculate the amount of time, in hours, they would spend waiting in line.

    Jonas found $\frac{2}{5} \times 10$.

    Frieda found $(2 \times 10) \div 5$.

    Rami found $2 \times (10 \div 5)$.

Which child wrote an expression that gives the correct solution? _____

Justify your answer.

_____

_____

_____

Words for the Wise

area	fraction	numerator
denominator	improper fraction	product
factor	mixed number	whole number

Be the best you can be!

⭐ partner practice

1. Michelle bought a package of 24 pencils. She took $\frac{11}{12}$ of the pencils to school and kept the rest at home. The equation represents the number of pencils Michelle took to school.

$$24 \times \frac{11}{12} = \boxed{}$$

Which procedure describes a correct way to find the missing number?

Ⓐ Divide 24 by 12 and then divide by 11.

Ⓑ Divide 24 by 12 and then multiply by 11.

Ⓒ Multiply 24 by 11 and then multiply by 12.

Ⓓ Multiply 24 by 12 and then divide by 11.

2. After her baby shower, Lindsey has $\frac{2}{5}$ of her cake left. She wants to give $\frac{1}{2}$ of the leftover cake to her best friend who helped with the shower. The model shows the cake.

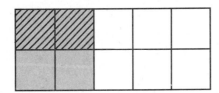

What portion of the whole cake will Lindsey give to her friend?

Ⓐ $\frac{4}{5}$ Ⓒ $\frac{3}{10}$

Ⓑ $\frac{2}{5}$ Ⓓ $\frac{1}{5}$

3. Three-sevenths of the Boomtown Bashers Soccer Team are girls. Two-thirds of the girls are ten years old. What fractional part of the soccer team is made up of ten-year-old girls?

Ⓐ $\frac{2}{7}$ Ⓒ $\frac{3}{5}$

Ⓑ $\frac{1}{2}$ Ⓓ $\frac{9}{14}$

4. Keesha ran $1\frac{1}{2}$ miles on Monday. She ran the same distance on Tuesday and only half the distance on Wednesday. Keesha recorded the expression, $2\frac{1}{2} \times 1\frac{1}{2}$ to represent the total distance she ran on the three days. She drew this number line to show the product.

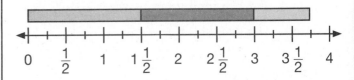

How far did Keesha run on the three days?

Ⓐ 3 mi

Ⓑ $3\frac{1}{2}$ mi

Ⓒ $3\frac{3}{4}$ mi

Ⓓ $4\frac{1}{2}$ mi

5. A rectangular game board is made up of equal-sized unit squares. The board is $2\frac{2}{3}$ feet long and 2 feet wide as shown here.

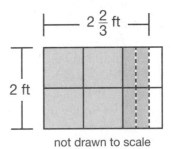

not drawn to scale

What is the area of the game board in square feet?

Ⓐ $\frac{8}{9}$ ft²

Ⓑ $4\frac{2}{3}$ ft²

Ⓒ $5\frac{1}{3}$ ft²

Ⓓ 10 ft²

 Level 5

1. Vic had 36 baseballs. He used $\frac{5}{6}$ of the balls at practice. The equation represents the number of balls Vic used at practice.

$$36 \times \frac{5}{6} = \square$$

Which procedure does **not** describe a correct way to find the product of this equation?

Ⓐ Use $\frac{5}{6}$ as an addend 36 times and find the sum.

Ⓑ Multiply 36 by 5 and then divide by 6.

Ⓒ Divide 36 by 6 and then multiply by 5.

Ⓓ Multiply 36 by 6 and then divide by 5.

2. Fred purchased a wooden board that was 1 foot long and 1 foot wide. He measured a rectangular piece of the board $\frac{3}{5}$ foot long and $\frac{2}{3}$ foot wide, as shown in the model. What is the total area of the piece of the board Fred measured, in square feet?

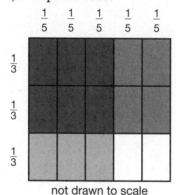

not drawn to scale

Ⓐ $\frac{2}{15}$ ft²   Ⓒ $\frac{2}{5}$ ft²

Ⓑ $\frac{1}{5}$ ft²   Ⓓ 1 ft²

3. Lilly wrote a 12-page report. She wrote $\frac{3}{4}$ of her report in black ink. Then her pen ran out of ink, and she had to switch to blue ink. How many pages did Lilly write in blue ink?

Ⓐ 1   Ⓒ 4

Ⓑ 3   Ⓓ 9

4. Allison is using a scrap piece of laminate flooring to tile the floor of her dollhouse with square tiles that are $\frac{1}{4}$ meter on each side. The outline of the floor with one tile is shown.

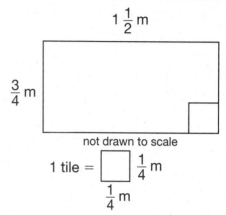

What is the area of the dollhouse floor, in square meters?

Ⓐ $1\frac{1}{8}$ m²   Ⓒ 18 m²

Ⓑ $1\frac{3}{8}$ m²   Ⓓ 24 m²

5. This rectangle is divided into squares that are $\frac{1}{6}$ meter long and $\frac{1}{6}$ meter wide.

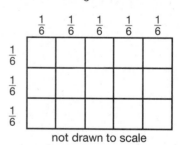

not drawn to scale

What is the total area of the rectangle in square meters?

Ⓐ $\frac{2}{5}$ m²   Ⓒ $\frac{15}{16}$ m²

Ⓑ $\frac{5}{12}$ m²   Ⓓ 3 m²

    Level 5

★ assessment

1. Tara sold candles to raise money for new playground equipment at her school. Tara's candle sales total $50, and the school will keep $\frac{2}{5}$ of that amount. The equation represents the dollars Tara earned for her school.

$$50 \times \frac{2}{5} = \boxed{}$$

Which expression does **not** show another way to find the product?

Ⓐ $(50 \times 2) \div 5$ Ⓒ $5 \times \frac{50}{2}$

Ⓑ $(50 \div 5) \times 2$ Ⓓ $2 \times \frac{50}{5}$

2. The Murphy Middle School band director took $\frac{3}{4}$ of the band members to a solo competition. The band director reports that $\frac{7}{9}$ of his band members who competed scored the top rating. This model represents the band members.

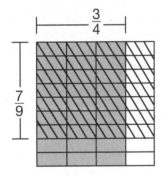

What fractional part of the Murphy Middle School band members scored the top rating at the solo competition?

Ⓐ $\frac{1}{3}$ Ⓒ $\frac{24}{36}$

Ⓑ $\frac{7}{12}$ Ⓓ $\frac{10}{13}$

3. Danielle uses carpet squares to create a rug as shown in the model. Each carpet square is $\frac{1}{2}$ yard by $\frac{1}{2}$ yard.

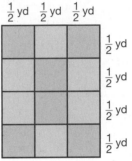

not drawn to scale

What is the area, in square yards, of Danielle's rug?

Ⓐ $\frac{1}{4}$ yd^2 Ⓒ 6 yd^2

Ⓑ 3 yd^2 Ⓓ 12 yd^2

4. Beverly cut two strips of ribbon that were each $1\frac{3}{4}$ yards long. Beverly recorded the expression $2 \times 1\frac{3}{4}$ to represent the total length of ribbon cut. She drew this number line to show the product.

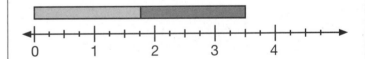

What is the total length of the ribbon cut?

Ⓐ $2\frac{1}{2}$ yd   Ⓒ $3\frac{1}{4}$ yd

Ⓑ $2\frac{3}{4}$ yd   Ⓓ $3\frac{1}{2}$ yd

5. Mr. Ballew's truck burns $\frac{3}{10}$ gallon of gasoline while he waits at red lights each day. How many gallons of gasoline will his truck burn at red lights over a 30-day period of time? Show your work.

Answer: _____

Analysis/Analyze

Jake is creating a design for a yearbook ad. He is using a piece of $\frac{1}{2}$-cm grid paper to draw his design. The outline of Jake's grid paper and one of the squares are shown.

Part A

Sketch squares along the length and width of the rectangle. Find the area of one square. Use this and your drawing to find the area of Jake's paper.

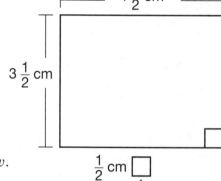

Area of 1 square = _____ cm²

Area of paper = _____ cm²

Part B

Now find the area of Jake's paper using the formula $A = l \times w$. Show your work.

Area of paper = _____ cm²

Compare the methods you used to find area in Part A and Part B. Which of these two methods do you find more useful, and why?

_____

_____

_____

Journal: Analysis/Analyze

Tristan said, "I think multiplying by $\frac{1}{2}$ is the same as dividing by 2."

Is Tristan correct? _____

Use words and numbers to explain your answer.

_____

_____

_____

★ **motivation station**

Fraction Action

Solve the fraction problems. Complete the models to find the solutions. Explain your thinking.

Two-thirds of the class made A's on the math test. Of the students who made A's, $\frac{1}{5}$ of them made a 100. What fraction of the students who earned A's made a 100 on the math test?
Shade the model to find the solution.

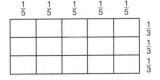

Answer:_____
Explanation

Five-tenths of the students have pets. One-fifth of the pets are cats. What fraction of the students have cats as pets?
Shade the model to find the solution.

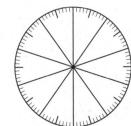

Answer:_____
Explanation

Mrs. McGregor is baking 6 batches of chocolate chip cookies for the school bake sale. Each batch uses $\frac{3}{4}$ cup of brown sugar. How many cups of brown sugar does Mrs. McGregor need?
Complete the model to find the solution.

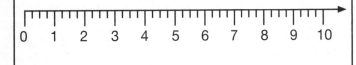

Answer:_____
Explanation

Wendy cuts a piece of paper in fourths. She takes one of the pieces, divides it into four equal sections, and colors one of the sections purple. What fraction of the paper is colored purple?
Shade the model to find the solution.

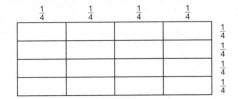

Answer:_____
Explanation

Parent Activities

1. Have your child roll 3 dice. Ask your child to create a fraction with two of the dice and then multiply it by the third die, which represents a whole number.

2. Using a dozen of any item at home, have your child practice grouping the items to find $\frac{1}{2}$, $\frac{1}{3}$, $\frac{1}{4}$, and $\frac{1}{6}$ dozen.

3. Arrange 100 pennies in a square array, with 10 pennies in each row. Turn $\frac{1}{2}$ of the pennies to heads and the rest to tails. Offer this challenge: "Half the pennies show heads. I will let you keep $\frac{3}{5}$ of the pennies that are heads if you can tell me how many that is." Show your child that 3 rows of heads equals $\frac{3}{5}$ of the heads. Since there are 10 pennies in each of the 3 rows, the answer is 30 pennies. Repeat with other challenges.

 Level 5

1. Marty is making an alien costume for a party. He needs $\frac{7}{8}$ yard of fabric and $1\frac{1}{2}$ yards of aluminum foil for the costume. Fabric costs $5 per yard. Will the fabric needed cost more than $5 or less than $5?

   Answer: _____

   Explain your answer. _____

   _____

2. The school cafeteria is 75 feet wide and 90 feet long. The school library has the same width but is 45 feet long. Without multiplying, explain how the area of the library compares with the area of the cafeteria.

   Answer: _____

   _____

   _____

   _____

3. How does the product of 55×90 compare to the product of 55×30? Explain how you can reach this conclusion by examining the factors instead of finding the products.

   Answer: _____

   _____

   _____

   _____

4. Yesterday, Ricardo ran one lap around the school track in $3\frac{1}{3}$ minutes. Today, he ran one lap in $\frac{7}{8}$ of yesterday's time. Did Ricardo's time increase or decrease from yesterday to today?

   Answer: _____

   Explain how you found your answer.

   _____

   _____

5. Marilyn's garden is 3 yards long and $\frac{2}{3}$ yard wide. Carolyn's garden is 3 yards long and $\frac{3}{2}$ yards wide. Is the area of Marilyn's garden larger or smaller than 3 square yards?

   Answer: _____

   Explain your answer.

   _____

   _____

   Is the area of Carolyn's garden larger or smaller than 3 square yards?

   Answer: _____

   Explain your answer.

   _____

   _____

   Draw pictures of the two gardens to verify your answers.

Words for the Wise

You're on top of it!

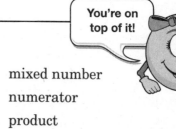

area	estimate	
denominator	factor	mixed number
dimension	fraction	numerator
equivalent	improper fraction	product

partner practice

1. Brandy has a new part-time job. On Monday, she worked $3\frac{3}{4}$ hours. On Wednesday, she worked twice as long as she did on Monday. Which **best** describes how long Brandy worked on Wednesday?

   Ⓐ less than 2 hours

   Ⓑ between 2 and $3\frac{3}{4}$ hours

   Ⓒ between 6 and 8 hours

   Ⓓ more than 8 hours

2. Greg wants to compare the area of a sticky note to the area of a note card. The sticky note is 3 inches long and 3 inches wide. The note card is 6 inches long and 3 inches wide. Which of these statements **best** compares the area of Greg's note card to the area of his sticky note?

   Ⓐ The area of the note card is less than half the area of the sticky note.

   Ⓑ The area of the note card is the same as the area of the sticky note.

   Ⓒ The area of the note card is double the area of the sticky note.

   Ⓓ The area of the note card is more than three times as much as the area of the sticky note.

3. How does the product of 364×12 compare to the product of 364×48?

   Ⓐ The product of 364×48 is twice the product of 364×12.

   Ⓑ The product of 364×12 is half the product of 364×48.

   Ⓒ The product of 364×12 is 4 times as much as the product of 364×48.

   Ⓓ The product of 364×48 is 4 times as much as the product of 364×12.

4. Star began with the number 240.6. She multiplied the number by $\frac{7}{5}$. Then Star multiplied that product by $\frac{13}{13}$. Which of the following is the most accurate statement?

   Ⓐ Star's number increased with the first multiplication and then remained the same with the second multiplication.

   Ⓑ The second product had a value of exactly 240.6.

   Ⓒ Star's number decreased with the first multiplication and then increased with the second multiplication.

   Ⓓ Star's number increased with the first multiplication and then increased again with the second multiplication.

5. Mrs. Calvin will choose $\frac{2}{5}$ of the third graders to participate in the school play. Mrs. Calvin wrote the fraction $\frac{50}{125}$ to show that 50 out of the school's 125 students would be chosen. How did Mrs. Calvin create the equivalent fraction $\frac{50}{125}$?

   Ⓐ She multiplied $\frac{2}{5}$ by 25.

   Ⓑ She added $\frac{48}{120}$ to $\frac{2}{5}$.

   Ⓒ She added 1 to $\frac{2}{5}$.

   Ⓓ She multiplied $\frac{2}{5}$ by $\frac{25}{25}$.

6. Stanley drinks $\frac{2}{3}$ cup of milk each day. Which **best** describes the amount of milk Stanley will drink in 5 days?

   Ⓐ $\frac{2}{3}$ cup

   Ⓑ between 3 and 5 cups

   Ⓒ exactly 5 cups

   Ⓓ more than 5 cups

 Level 5

1. Makayla's favorite cookie recipe requires $2\frac{1}{8}$ cups of sugar to make 24 cookies. She wants to make 48 cookies for her classmates. Which **best** describes the amount of sugar Makayla will need?

   Ⓐ less than $2\frac{1}{8}$ cups

   Ⓑ between $2\frac{1}{8}$ and 4 cups

   Ⓒ between 4 and 5 cups

   Ⓓ greater than 6 cups

2. Alli created a rectangular photo collage that was 25 inches long and 18 inches wide. Jayden created a rectangular photo collage that was 25 inches long and 36 inches wide. Which of these statements **best** compares the area of Jayden's collage with the area of Alli's collage?

   Ⓐ The area of Jayden's collage is half the area of Alli's collage.

   Ⓑ The area of Jayden's collage is about the same as the area of Alli's collage.

   Ⓒ The area of Jayden's collage is twice the area of Alli's collage.

   Ⓓ The area of Jayden's collage is three times as much as the area of Alli's collage.

3. How does the product of 75×15 compare to the product of 75×45?

   Ⓐ The product of 75×45 is twice the product of 75×15.

   Ⓑ The product of 75×15 is half the product of 75×45.

   Ⓒ The product of 75×15 is $\frac{1}{4}$ as much as the product of 75×45.

   Ⓓ The product of 75×45 is 3 times as much as the product of 75×15.

4. Kwan spent 27 minutes talking on the phone on Wednesday. On Thursday, Kwan's phone time was $\frac{9}{10}$ of Wednesday's time. On Friday, Kwan's phone time was $\frac{10}{9}$ of Wednesday's time. Which of the following most accurately compares Kwan's phone times on Thursday and Friday with his phone time on Wednesday?

   Ⓐ Kwan's phone time increased on Thursday and increased again on Friday.

   Ⓑ Kwan's phone time decreased on Thursday and decreased again on Friday.

   Ⓒ Kwan's phone time increased on Thursday and decreased on Friday.

   Ⓓ Kwan's phone time decreased on Thursday and increased on Friday.

5. Rylan completes these calculations.

   $$\frac{5}{8} = \frac{5 \times 6}{8 \times 6} = \frac{30}{48}$$

   Rylan concludes that $\frac{5}{8}$ is equivalent to $\frac{30}{48}$. Which statement **best** applies?

   Ⓐ Rylan is correct because $\frac{6}{6} = 1$.

   Ⓑ Rylan is incorrect because $30 > 5$ and $48 > 8$.

   Ⓒ Rylan is correct because $\frac{5}{8}$ is less than 1.

   Ⓓ Rylan is incorrect because 6 is greater than 1.

6. Daniel used $\frac{5}{8}$ of a box of nails to build a treehouse. A box of nails weighs 16 ounces. Which statement is true about the weight of the nails Daniel used?

   Ⓐ Daniel used less than 16 ounces of nails.

   Ⓑ Daniel used exactly 1 pound of nails.

   Ⓒ Daniel used more than 16 ounces of nails.

   Ⓓ Daniel used about 2 ounces of nails.

★ assessment

1. Donut King sells glazed donuts for $6 per dozen. Ellen buys $2\frac{3}{4}$ dozen. Which statement is true about the number of donuts Ellen buys?

Ⓐ Ellen buys fewer than 12 donuts.

Ⓑ Ellen buys more than 12 but less than 24 donuts.

Ⓒ Ellen buys more than 24 but less than 36 donuts.

Ⓓ Ellen buys more than 36 donuts.

2. Shera cut a rectangular piece of poster board 2 feet long by $2\frac{1}{2}$ feet wide for her art project. Chen cut a rectangular piece of poster board 2 feet long by $1\frac{1}{4}$ feet wide for his art project. Which **best** compares the area of Chen's board with the area of Shera's board?

Ⓐ The area of Chen's board is one-fourth the area of Shera's board.

Ⓑ The area of Chen's board is half the area of Shera's board.

Ⓒ The area of Chen's board is $1\frac{1}{4}$ square feet less than the area of Shera's board.

Ⓓ The area of Chen's board is double the area of Shera's board.

3. Jacob's backpack weighs 8 kilograms. Emma's backpack weighs $\frac{2}{3}$ as much as Jacob's backpack. Which is a correct estimate of the weight of Emma's backpack?

Ⓐ less than 4 kilograms

Ⓑ between 4 and 8 kilograms

Ⓒ exactly 8 kilograms

Ⓓ greater than 8 kilograms

4. Arnold's Hot Dog Stand sold $8014 in hot dogs during the month of June. Arnold's July sales were $1\frac{1}{8}$ times as much as his June sales. Arnold's August sales were $\frac{9}{10}$ as much as his July sales. Which of the following is the most accurate statement comparing June sales with the other two months?

Ⓐ Arnold's sales increased in July and increased again in August.

Ⓑ Arnold's sales decreased in July and decreased again in August.

Ⓒ Arnold's sales decreased in July and increased in August.

Ⓓ Arnold's sales increased in July and decreased in August.

5. Alan had two mirrors installed in his house. The first mirror was 2 yards tall and $\frac{2}{3}$ yard wide. The second mirror was 2 yards tall and $\frac{3}{2}$ yards wide. Which mirror has the greatest area?

Answer: _____

Is the area of the first mirror greater than or less than 2 square yards?

Answer: _____

Is the area of the second mirror greater than or less than 2 square yards?

Answer: _____

Draw pictures to justify your answers.

Analysis/Analyze

1. In the multiplication puzzle shown, each square stands for the same number from 1-5. Find the number that can be placed in each square in order to solve the puzzle.

$$\frac{3}{4} \times \frac{2}{\square} < \frac{3}{4}$$

$$\frac{2}{\square} \times \frac{\square}{4} > \frac{2}{\square}$$

$$\frac{\square}{4} \times \frac{4}{\square} = 1$$

Answer: _____

Explain why the number you chose is correct and the other four numbers are not correct.

_____

_____

Synthesis/Create

2. Write a story problem in which the product is greater than 2. Your story must include at least one fraction.

_____

_____

_____

Journal: Analysis/Analyze

Without multiplying, do you think the product of 0.86×14 is greater than 14 or less than 14? Explain your thinking.

_____

_____

_____

★ **motivation station**

On a Roll

Play *On a Roll* with a partner. Each player needs a pencil. Each pair of players needs a number cube and the game board below. In turn, players roll the number cube and solve the corresponding problem by drawing a picture to prove the answer. The player is awarded the number of points in the banner next to the problem. If a player rolls the number of a problem that has already been solved, play passes to the next player. The winner is the player with the most points after all problems have been solved.

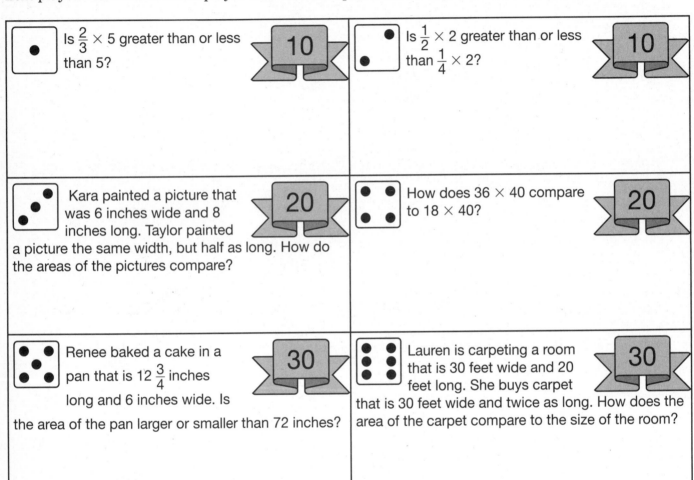

Is $\frac{2}{3} \times 5$ greater than or less than 5?   **10**

Is $\frac{1}{2} \times 2$ greater than or less than $\frac{1}{4} \times 2$?   **10**

Kara painted a picture that was 6 inches wide and 8 inches long. Taylor painted a picture the same width, but half as long. How do the areas of the pictures compare?   **20**

How does 36×40 compare to 18×40?   **20**

Renee baked a cake in a pan that is $12\frac{3}{4}$ inches long and 6 inches wide. Is the area of the pan larger or smaller than 72 inches?   **30**

Lauren is carpeting a room that is 30 feet wide and 20 feet long. She buys carpet that is 30 feet wide and twice as long. How does the area of the carpet compare to the size of the room?   **30**

Parent Activities

1. Use square sticky notes to create a rectangle that is 10 notes long and 8 notes wide. The total number of notes represents the area, since $10 \times 8 = 80$. Ask your child to predict what will happen to the area of the rectangle if you reduce the length to 5, but leave the width the same. Show your child that this would result in a rectangle with an area that could be expressed as 5×8. Since 40 is half of 80, encourage your child to draw the conclusion that reducing the length to half of the original length would also reduce the area to half the total area of the original rectangle.

2. Fold a sheet of paper into fourths. Open the paper, draw lines along the creases, and label each section as $\frac{1}{4}$. Next draw a line segment through each folded section to form 8 total sections. Count the number of eighths needed to make each fourth. Show that $\frac{1}{4} = \frac{2}{8}$, and discuss that $\frac{1}{4}$ can be multiplied by $\frac{2}{2}$ to find the equivalent fraction.

       Level 5

1. Mr. Mullins purchased $3\frac{1}{2}$ pounds of hot dogs. He used $\frac{2}{3}$ of the hot dogs for his son's birthday party. How many pounds of hot dogs did Mr. Mullins use?

   Answer: _____

2. It takes Myrna one hour to decorate $3\frac{1}{4}$ dozen cookies. How many dozen cookies can Myrna decorate in $2\frac{1}{3}$ hours?

   Answer: _____ dozen cookies

   How many single cookies are equal to your answer?

   Answer: _____ cookies

3. Diana watched a $3\frac{1}{6}$-hour DVD, as shown on the number line.

   When $\frac{1}{2}$ of the movie had played, Diana fell asleep. How many hours of the movie did Diana watch?

   Answer: _____ hours

   How many minutes of the movie did Diana watch?

   Answer: _____ minutes

4. Jace used a poster board for his history project. The dimensions are shown in the diagram.

   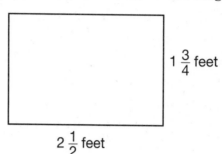

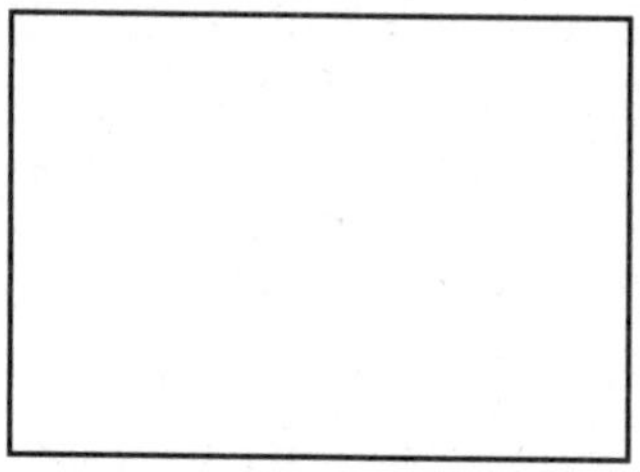

   $1\frac{3}{4}$ feet

   $2\frac{1}{2}$ feet

   not drawn to scale

   Determine the area of Jace's poster board in square feet.

   Answer: _____

5. Jane spent $3\frac{3}{4}$ hours helping her mom with chores. She spent $\frac{3}{5}$ of that time washing and putting away laundry. How many minutes did Jane spend on laundry?

   Answer: _____ minutes

   Explain how you found your answer.

   _____

   _____

   _____

Words for the Wise

The possibilities are endless!

area	improper fraction	numerator
denominator	lowest terms	product
factor	mixed number	proper fraction

★ partner practice

1. Marta wants to use her mother's recipe for chicken tortilla soup. Her mother's recipe makes enough soup for 10-12 people, but Marta wants to make only $\frac{1}{3}$ that amount. If the original recipe requires $2\frac{1}{2}$ pounds of chicken, how many pounds of chicken will Marta need for her soup?

Ⓐ $\frac{5}{6}$ lb

Ⓒ $2\frac{5}{6}$ lb

Ⓑ $2\frac{1}{6}$ lb

Ⓓ $20\frac{1}{2}$ lb

2. A salesperson for Ace Computer Company reports the company's sales were about $2\frac{3}{5}$ million dollars in 2000. Eleven years later, Ace's sales were $4\frac{1}{2}$ times as much. Which of these mixed numbers should the salesperson use to represent Ace's 2011 sales, in millions of dollars?

Ⓐ $8\frac{1}{5}$

Ⓒ $10\frac{11}{17}$

Ⓑ $8\frac{3}{10}$

Ⓓ $11\frac{7}{10}$

3. Adair had $6\frac{1}{2}$ cups of tomato juice in his refrigerator, as shown in this diagram.

He used $\frac{4}{5}$ of the juice to make soup. How many cups of tomato juice did Adair use to make soup?

Ⓐ $5\frac{1}{5}$ cups

Ⓒ $6\frac{2}{5}$ cups

Ⓑ $5\frac{2}{5}$ cups

Ⓓ $6\frac{4}{5}$ cups

4. The length of this poster board is $1\frac{2}{3}$ times its width. What is the area of the poster board, in square feet?

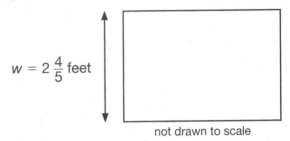

$w = 2\frac{4}{5}$ feet

not drawn to scale

Ⓐ $1\frac{2}{5}$ ft^2

Ⓒ $7\frac{7}{9}$ ft^2

Ⓑ $4\frac{2}{3}$ ft^2

Ⓓ $13\frac{1}{15}$ ft^2

5. Harry ran 15 miles in $15\frac{1}{2}$ minutes. Tomas ran the same distance in $\frac{7}{8}$ of Harry's time. How many minutes did it take Tomas to run 15 miles?

Ⓐ $\frac{7}{16}$ min

Ⓒ $13\frac{9}{16}$ min

Ⓑ $13\frac{1}{8}$ min

Ⓓ $16\frac{3}{8}$ min

6. Mort can make $5\frac{3}{4}$ bookmarks in 1 hour. How many bookmarks can Mort make in $3\frac{1}{2}$ hours?

Ⓐ $1\frac{1}{4}$

Ⓒ $15\frac{3}{8}$

Ⓑ $9\frac{1}{4}$

Ⓓ $20\frac{1}{8}$

 Level 5

1. Mrs. Myers prepared $4\frac{1}{2}$ quarts of soup. She took $\frac{2}{5}$ of the soup to her neighbor. How many quarts of soup did Mrs. Myers take to her neighbor?

   Ⓐ $\frac{2}{5}$ qt   Ⓒ $1\frac{4}{5}$ qt

   Ⓑ $1\frac{4}{7}$ qt   Ⓓ $4\frac{1}{5}$ qt

2. Bill collected $3\frac{1}{3}$ pounds of cans for recycling on Monday and $2\frac{3}{4}$ pounds of cans on Tuesday. Rodney helped him on Wednesday, and they collected $2\frac{2}{5}$ times as much as Bill collected on Monday. How many pounds of cans did Bill and Rodney collect on Wednesday?

   Ⓐ $6\frac{2}{15}$ lb   Ⓒ $10\frac{1}{5}$ lb

   Ⓑ 8 lb   Ⓓ $13\frac{1}{5}$ lb

3. Jake and his father were clearing an area in their backyard to build a 7-foot tall wooden fort. They marked off a rectangle $6\frac{1}{4}$ feet by $10\frac{2}{5}$ feet. How many square feet of the yard are Jake and his father planning to use to build the fort?

   Ⓐ $60\frac{1}{10}$ ft²   Ⓒ 65 ft²

   Ⓑ $60\frac{3}{20}$ ft²   Ⓓ 75 ft²

4. A bridge designer created plans for a bridge that would be $1\frac{2}{3}$ miles long, as shown here.

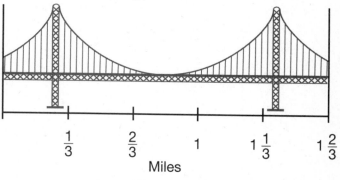

$\frac{1}{3}$ $\frac{2}{3}$ 1 $1\frac{1}{3}$ $1\frac{2}{3}$

Miles

not drawn to scale

After 6 months of construction, the project manager reported that $\frac{3}{4}$ of the bridge was complete. How many miles of the bridge had been completed?

   Ⓐ $1\frac{1}{4}$ mi   Ⓒ $1\frac{5}{7}$ mi

   Ⓑ $1\frac{1}{2}$ mi   Ⓓ $4\frac{1}{2}$ mi

5. One scientist estimates the total weight of all biological material on the earth to be about $74\frac{1}{2}$ billion tons. She reports that farm animals represent about $\frac{1}{10}$ of the total weight, while crops represent about $\frac{3}{10}$ of the total weight. According to the scientist, how many billion tons do all farm animals and crops on earth weigh?

   Ⓐ $29\frac{4}{5}$ Ⓒ $14\frac{9}{10}$

   Ⓑ $22\frac{7}{20}$ Ⓓ $2\frac{47}{200}$

assessment

1. Rachel purchased $1\frac{1}{2}$ pounds of grapes and 2 pounds of apples. She took $\frac{1}{5}$ of the grapes to school in her lunch box. How many pounds of grapes did Rachel take in her lunch box?

Ⓐ $1\frac{1}{10}$ lb

Ⓑ $\frac{7}{10}$ lb

Ⓒ $\frac{2}{5}$ lb

Ⓓ $\frac{3}{10}$ lb

2. Rhett estimates it will take him $3\frac{1}{3}$ hours to complete his science fair project as shown on this number line.

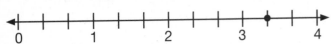

Rhett plans to spend $\frac{2}{5}$ of that time on his experiment. How many hours will Rhett spend on his experiment?

Ⓐ $\frac{2}{5}$ hr

Ⓑ $1\frac{1}{3}$ hr

Ⓒ $1\frac{2}{3}$ hr

Ⓓ $2\frac{1}{3}$ hr

3. In a photograph, Kelsey is $7\frac{1}{2}$ inches tall. Her actual height is $8\frac{1}{5}$ times as tall as she appears in the photo. How tall is Kelsey, in inches?

Ⓐ $61\frac{1}{2}$ in

Ⓒ $56\frac{2}{7}$ in

Ⓑ $61\frac{1}{10}$ in

Ⓓ $56\frac{1}{10}$ in

4. This figure shows the dimensions of Mr. Bryant's television.

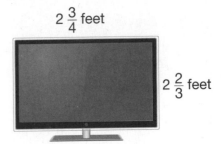

What is the area of Mr. Bryant's television screen in square feet?

Ⓐ $4\frac{1}{2}$ ft²

Ⓒ $6\frac{1}{2}$ ft²

Ⓑ $4\frac{3}{4}$ ft²

Ⓓ $7\frac{1}{3}$ ft²

5. Stephen's soccer practice lasted $2\frac{1}{2}$ hours. If Stephen spent $\frac{3}{4}$ of the practice time kicking goals, how many minutes did he spend kicking goals?

Answer: _____ minutes

Explain how you found your answer.

_____

_____

         Level 5   ©2012–2013 MentoringMinds.com

Analysis/Analyze

1. Mel's teacher put a multiplication puzzle with mixed numbers on the math test. Mel wrote the same number in each box to make this equation true.

$$\square\frac{\square}{4} \times 2\frac{1}{\square} = 8\frac{\square}{4}$$

What number did Mel write in the boxes?

Answer _____

Explain how you found your answer.

_____

_____

Analysis/Analyze

2. Jeremiah wrote this sequence of numbers.

$\frac{2}{3}$, $1\frac{1}{3}$, 2, $2\frac{2}{3}$, $3\frac{1}{3}$, 4

Zachary wrote this sequence of numbers.

1, $1\frac{1}{4}$, $1\frac{1}{2}$, $1\frac{3}{4}$, 2

What is the product of the tenth terms of these sequences?

Answer _____

Journal: Analysis/Analyze

Serena drew a rectangular picture in her art class. The length of the drawing was $8\frac{1}{2}$ inches and the width was $6\frac{1}{2}$ inches. Serena said the area of her picture was $48\frac{1}{4}$ square inches. Explain why Serena was incorrect.

_____

_____

_____

_____

★ motivation station

Pizza Factory

Play *Pizza Factory* with the whole class. Each player needs a pencil or crayon and the game board below. The teacher signals start to begin the game. Players solve each fraction problem and color the pepperoni that matches the answer, labeling it with the matching problem number. The winner is the first person to correctly color all the pepperonis.

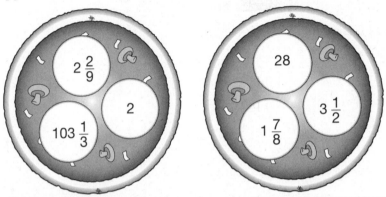

Problem	Solution
1. Miguel has $2\frac{1}{2}$ pizzas. $\frac{3}{4}$ of the pizzas have pepperonis. What fraction of the pizzas have pepperonis?	
2. Frank has 6 pizzas. $\frac{1}{3}$ of the pizzas have stuffed crust. How many pizzas have stuffed crust?	
3. Mrs. Nelson's class drank $3\frac{1}{3}$ gallons of soda. $\frac{2}{3}$ of the soda was orange soda. How much soda was orange?	
4. The pizza buffet has 5 pizzas. $\frac{7}{10}$ of the buffet is eaten by the time Mrs. Nelson's class left. How many pizzas did Mrs. Nelson's class eat?	
5. The cook makes a rectangular pizza that is $10\frac{1}{3}$ inches long and 10 inches wide. What is the area of the pizza?	
6. Each pizza calls for $2\frac{1}{3}$ cup of sauce. How many cups of sauce are needed to make 12 pizzas?	

Parent Activities

1. Ask your child to weigh a bag of fruits or vegetables on a grocery scale. Use multiplication to predict what will happen to the weight when half the items are removed from the bag. For example, "If a whole bag of pears weighs $3\frac{1}{2}$ pounds, how much would half a bag weigh?" Your child can predict the weight of half a bag by multiplying $\frac{1}{2} \times 3\frac{1}{2}$. Remove half the items and weigh the bag again to see how close your child's prediction is to the actual weight.

2. Look for a shelf of reduced items in the store. If, for example, the items are reduced to $\frac{1}{4}$ of their original price, help your child see that the sale price can be calculated by multiplying the original price by $\frac{1}{4}$.

 Level 5

1. Reynaldo bought a 1-yard rope of strawberry licorice candy, as shown in the diagram. Reynaldo and his 3 sisters equally shared $\frac{1}{4}$ of the candy on Monday.

```
0        1/4       1/2       3/4      1 yd
        not drawn to scale
```

The fraction of the 1-yard rope Reynaldo ate on Monday equals $\frac{1}{4} \div 4$. What fractional part of the licorice rope did Reynaldo eat?

Answer: _____

2. Mrs. Post baked a rectangular cake. She cut the cake into 3 equal sections and gave $\frac{1}{3}$ of the cake to her neighbor, Mrs. Otto. Mrs. Otto cut her section of cake into 8 equal pieces as shown in the model.

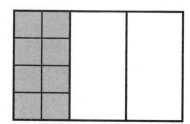

Each piece is a fractional part of the original cake. Complete the equation to show the fractional part of the whole cake represented by each of Mrs. Otto's pieces.

Answer: _____ ÷ _____ = _____

3. During the 1-hour telethon, 10 minutes were allotted for commercials from sponsors. Each commercial was $\frac{1}{2}$ minute long. How many commercials can be scheduled for the allotted 10 minutes?

Answer: _____

4. Dixon correctly drew a model to match this equation.

$$3 \div \frac{1}{5} = 15$$

Draw a model Dixon could have used.

5. Sara's mom has $\frac{1}{2}$ of a pot of chili left after dinner. She wants to divide it into 3 equal servings for lunch the next day. What fractional part of the original pot of chili does each serving of leftover chili represent?

Answer: _____

Words for the Wise

denominator	fraction
dividend	numerator
divisor	quotient

unit fraction

You learned it correctly!

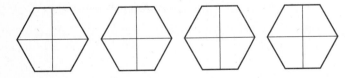

1. Antonio drew a model to illustrate an expression and find its value.

Which equation correctly matches Antonio's model?

Ⓐ $\frac{1}{4} \div 4 = \frac{1}{16}$

Ⓑ $16 \div \frac{1}{4} = 64$

Ⓒ $4 \div \frac{1}{4} = 16$

Ⓓ $16 \times 4 = 64$

2. Jeremy cuts a poster board into sevenths in order to create mats for his artwork. Then he cuts each seventh into 3 equal pieces. The model represents how Jeremy cut the poster board. The shaded section shows $\frac{1}{7}$ of the poster board.

Each piece is a fractional part of the original poster board. Which equation correctly shows the fractional part represented by each piece?

Ⓐ $\frac{1}{7} \div 3 = \frac{1}{21}$

Ⓑ $\frac{1}{7} \div 3 = \frac{3}{21}$

Ⓒ $3 \times \frac{1}{7} = \frac{3}{7}$

Ⓓ $7 \div 3 = \frac{7}{3}$

3. The Wilsons are having a cookout. Mrs. Wilson buys 10 pounds of ground meat to make hamburgers. She plans to make $\frac{1}{3}$-pound burgers for the party. How many burgers will Mrs. Wilson be able to make?

Ⓐ $\frac{10}{3}$

Ⓒ 30

Ⓑ 3

Ⓓ 60

4. Celia solved a problem using this equation.

$$\frac{1}{3} \div 3 = \frac{1}{9}$$

Which could have been Celia's problem?

Ⓐ Sarah finished $\frac{1}{3}$ of her homework before dinner. If she had 3 pages of homework, how many pages did Sarah complete before dinner?

Ⓑ The Poff family plans to rake $\frac{1}{3}$ of their yard on Saturday. If each of the 3 family members rakes an equal area, what fraction of the yard will each member of the Poff family rake?

Ⓒ Dan had 3 bags of erasers. He gave $\frac{1}{3}$ of a bag to his friend. How many bags of erasers does Dan have now?

Ⓓ Mrs. Sertain has 3 cups of cherries for tarts. She uses $\frac{1}{3}$ cup of cherries for each tart. How many tarts can Mrs. Sertain make?

5. Ten children visited Grandma after school. Grandma served the children cookies and milk. Grandma divided $\frac{1}{2}$ gallon of milk into 10 equal glasses for the children. What fractional part of a gallon of milk did each child receive?

Ⓐ $\frac{1}{20}$ gal

Ⓒ $\frac{1}{5}$ gal

Ⓑ $\frac{1}{10}$ gal

Ⓓ $\frac{1}{2}$ gal

 Level 5

1. Marie has 2 spools of ribbon. One spool holds 3 yards of ribbon, and the other spool holds 2 yards of ribbon. She uses all the ribbon to cut bookmarks that are each $\frac{1}{4}$ yard long. How many bookmarks does Marie make?

   Ⓐ 5   Ⓒ 15

   Ⓑ 10   Ⓓ 20

2. Marco drew a model to illustrate an expression and find its value.

   Which equation correctly matches Marco's model?

   Ⓐ $\frac{1}{8} \div 4 = \frac{1}{32}$ Ⓒ $\frac{1}{2} \div 8 = \frac{1}{16}$

   Ⓑ $\frac{1}{4} \div 2 = \frac{1}{8}$ Ⓓ $8 \div \frac{1}{4} = 32$

3. Isabella is cutting yarn from a roll for an art project. She has $\frac{1}{9}$ of a roll of red yarn, and she cuts it into 4 equal pieces. What fractional part of the original roll of yarn is represented by each of Isabella's pieces?

   Ⓐ $\frac{1}{36}$ Ⓒ $\frac{9}{4}$

   Ⓑ $\frac{4}{9}$ Ⓓ 36

4. Eli correctly solved a problem using this equation.

   $$9 \div \frac{1}{3} = 27$$

   Which of these problems could Eli have solved?

   Ⓐ Nicole caught 9 fish. Each fish weighed $\frac{1}{3}$ pound. What was the total weight of Nicole's fish?

   Ⓑ Crystal rode her scooter $\frac{1}{3}$ mile for 9 days in a row. How far did Crystal ride her scooter during the 9 days?

   Ⓒ Wayne prepared 9 cups of banana pudding. He served the pudding in small bowls with $\frac{1}{3}$ cup pudding per bowl. How many bowls of pudding could Wayne serve?

   Ⓓ Mr. Lee had $\frac{1}{3}$ of a piece of sheet metal. He cut the sheet metal into 9 equal rectangles for repairing his work shed. What fractional part of a whole piece of sheet metal was represented by each rectangle?

5. Braden bought a 20-pound bag of colored sand to put into his sand pit. Braden's bucket can hold $\frac{1}{2}$ pound of sand. How many times will Braden need to fill his bucket in order to carry all the sand from the bag to his sand pit?

   Ⓐ 8   Ⓒ 20

   Ⓑ 10   Ⓓ 40

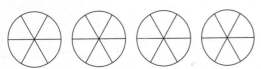

assessment

1. Franci drew a model to illustrate an expression and find its value.

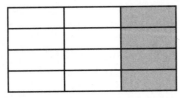

Which equation correctly matches Franci's model?

Ⓐ $\frac{1}{6} \div 4 = \frac{1}{24}$

Ⓒ $\frac{1}{6} \times 4 = \frac{2}{3}$

Ⓑ $24 \times \frac{1}{6} = \frac{1}{4}$

Ⓓ $4 \div \frac{1}{6} = 24$

2. Mr. Cameron has $\frac{1}{3}$ of a pan of lasagna, represented by the shaded part of the rectangle. He cuts the lasagna into 4 equal pieces for himself and his 3 children. This model shows how Mr. Cameron cut the lasagna. Each share represents $\frac{1}{3} \div 4$.

What is the value of the expression $\frac{1}{3} \div 4$?

Ⓐ $\frac{1}{12}$

Ⓒ $\frac{4}{3}$

Ⓑ $\frac{3}{4}$

Ⓓ 12

3. Mrs. Acker baked muffins. She added $\frac{1}{2}$ cup sugar to the muffin batter and then divided the batter equally into the 12 sections of the muffin pan. What fraction of a cup of sugar will each muffin contain?

Ⓐ 24 cups

Ⓒ $\frac{1}{12}$ cup

Ⓑ $\frac{1}{6}$ cup

Ⓓ $\frac{1}{24}$ cup

4. Kirk solved a problem using this equation.

$$\frac{1}{10} \div 10 = \frac{1}{100}$$

Which problem could Kirk have solved?

Ⓐ Allie wrote $\frac{1}{10}$ page of a report every day. What fractional part of the report did Allie write in 10 days?

Ⓑ Billy had 10 pages of photos. Each photo represented $\frac{1}{10}$ of a page. How many photos did Billy have?

Ⓒ Contessa had $\frac{1}{10}$ of a bag of gerbil food. She divided the food into equal portions, so that her gerbil had a 10-day supply of food. What fraction of a bag of food did Contessa's gerbil receive during each of the 10 days?

Ⓓ Danny served a pie to 10 people. He noticed that $\frac{1}{10}$ of the pie was left. If each person ate the same amount of pie, what fractional part of the pie did each of the 10 people eat?

5. A quarter is $\frac{1}{16}$-inch thick. Roderick has a stack of quarters 8 inches high. How many quarters does Roderick have?

Answer: _____

 Level 5

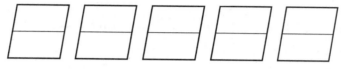

Synthesis/Create

1. Create a division story that can be illustrated with this diagram. Your story must include the fraction $\frac{1}{2}$. Then write an equation to show the solution to your story.

_____

_____

_____

Synthesis/Create

2. Create a short story to illustrate this expression: $\frac{1}{2} \div 4$

_____

_____

_____

Then use this diagram to show your quotient.

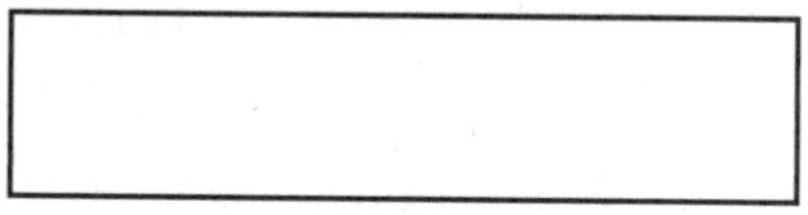

Explain the relationship between your diagram and your story.

_____

_____

Journal: Analysis/Analyze

Javier and Mary purchased a 6-pound bag of dog food for their dog Rex. Rex eats $\frac{1}{3}$ pound of food per day. Javier and Mary want to know how many days the bag of food will last. Javier believes they can solve their problem using the expression $6 \div \frac{1}{3}$, but Mary wants to use the expression $\frac{1}{3} \div 6$. Who is correct, and why?

_____

_____

_____

Name _____

What's Your Story?

Create story contexts for the expressions. Solve the story contexts and draw models to prove that the solution is correct. Share the problems and solutions with the class.

Story	Model	Solution
$7 \div \dfrac{2}{3}$		
$\dfrac{1}{4} \div 3$		
$3 \div \dfrac{5}{8}$		

Parent Activities

1. Look at the wrapper on a stick of butter. Point out that the whole stick represents $\dfrac{1}{2}$ cup. Notice that the stick is divided into 8 equal pieces. Help your child determine that each piece would represent $\dfrac{1}{16}$ of a whole cup of butter. This can be expressed as $\dfrac{1}{2} \div 8 = \dfrac{1}{16}$.

2. Use a dozen eggs to ask your child questions involving fractions, such as, "If 3 people share $\dfrac{1}{2}$ carton of eggs, how many eggs will each person receive?" and "If we have 2 cartons of eggs and each person gets $\dfrac{1}{4}$ carton of eggs for breakfast, how many people can we feed?"

3. Look on food labels to find items with fractional serving sizes, such as "1 serving = $\dfrac{1}{4}$ cup." Discuss how many of these servings would be needed if you wanted 2, 3, or 4 of the unit of measurement used.

1. Jeff made fruit punch using 1 quart of orange juice, 2 pints of pineapple juice, 8 cups of tropical punch, and 8 pints of ginger ale. How many gallons of fruit punch did Jeff make?

   Answer: _____

2. This table shows the number of miles that Leah jogged last week.

Day	Distance
Monday	2 miles
Wednesday	3 miles
Thursday	5 miles

   How many yards did Leah jog last week?

   Answer: _____

3. Mrs. Gallegos made lemonade. She filled a 2-quart pitcher three times with cold water. How many cups of water were in Mrs. Gallegos's lemonade?

   Answer: _____

   Write a sentence explaining the steps you used to find your answer.

   _____

   _____

4. Sigourney cut a 4.4-meter strip of wallpaper border into four pieces. The first piece was 92 centimeters long, and the second piece was 154 centimeters long. The third piece was 890 millimeters long. How many centimeters long was the remaining piece?

   Answer: _____

5. When Eduardo was sick, the doctor told him to take 25 milliliters of medicine the first day. After that, Eduardo must take 5 milliliters of the medicine three times each day. How many liters of medicine will Eduardo take in 10 days?

   Answer: _____

6. Doreen walks 5 kilometers on a treadmill every day after work. How many meters will Doreen walk on the treadmill in 5 days?

   Answer: _____

You're the expert!

Words for the Wise

capacity	inch (in)	milligram (mg)
centimeter (cm)	kilogram (kg)	milliliter (mL)
cup	kilometer (km)	minute (min)
customary system	liquid volume	ounce (oz)
equivalent	liter (L)	pint (pt)
foot/feet (ft)	mass	pound (lb)
gallon (gal)	meter (m)	quart (qt)
gram (g)	metric system	second (s)
hour (hr)	mile (mi)	yard (yd)

★ partner practice

1. Kaylea is making punch for 60 students in the band. Her recipe makes enough for 15 servings and uses 3 quarts of orange soda. How many gallons of orange soda will Kaylea need to serve all 60 students?

   Ⓐ 12 gal

   Ⓑ 6 gal

   Ⓒ 4 gal

   Ⓓ 3 gal

2. According to Tamika's countdown clock, 1 day, 4 hours, 17 minutes, and 7 seconds remain until her birthday party. How many seconds does Tamika have to wait until her party?

   Ⓐ 1,697.7 s

   Ⓑ 91,827 s

   Ⓒ 101,827 s

   Ⓓ 231,427 s

3. Al purchased 2.12 kilograms of food pellets for the animals in the petting zoo. Al gave 177 grams of food pellets to the rabbits and 276 grams to the chickens. He gave 0.1 kilogram of pellets to the ducks and 619 grams to the goats. Al gave all of the remaining food to the calves. How many kilograms of food pellets did Al give to the calves?

   Ⓐ 0.948 kg

   Ⓑ 94.8 kg

   Ⓒ 948 kg

   Ⓓ 1047.9 kg

4. Zachary volunteers at the animal shelter on weekends. One Saturday, Zachary unloaded 38 bags of dog food. Each bag weighed 25 pounds. How many ounces of dog food did Zachary unload?

   Ⓐ 400 oz   Ⓒ 11,400 oz

   Ⓑ 950 oz   Ⓓ 15,200 oz

5. Jacobi's father drives a truck 4 days each week. The table shows the driving record for one week.

   Weekly Driving Record

Day	Distance Traveled
Monday	30.51 km
Tuesday	105.4 km
Wednesday	80.75 km
Thursday	64.6 km

   What is the total number of meters Jacobi's father drove?

   Ⓐ 28.126 m   Ⓒ 28,126 m

   Ⓑ 281.26 m   Ⓓ 281,260 m

6. Brandon drank two 2-liter bottles of soda. How can Brandon find the total number of milliliters of soda he drank?

   Ⓐ Multiply 2 and 2, then add 1000.

   Ⓑ Divide 1000 by the product of 2 and 2.

   Ⓒ Multiply 2 and 1000, then divide by 4.

   Ⓓ Multiply 2 and 1000, then double the product.

1. Weston and Keaton collected aluminum cans for 4 weeks. The table shows the weight, in ounces, each boy collected every week.

Aluminum Can Log

	Weston	Keaton
Week 1	48 oz	56 oz
Week 2	96 oz	64 oz
Week 3	72 oz	32 oz
Week 4	144 oz	112 oz

What is the total weight, in pounds, of cans collected by the boys?

Ⓐ $22\frac{1}{2}$ lb   Ⓒ 39 lb

Ⓑ 36 lb   Ⓓ 624 lb

2. The Cougars football team drank $2\frac{1}{2}$ cases of bottled water during a practice. Each case contained 24 bottles of water, and each bottle held 1 pint. How many gallons of water did the Cougars drink during the practice?

Ⓐ 7 gal   Ⓒ 8 gal

Ⓑ $7\frac{1}{2}$ gal   Ⓓ $8\frac{1}{2}$ gal

3. Martina can run 9 miles without stopping. Last year she could run 36,960 feet without stopping. How many more yards can Martina run now than she could run last year?

Ⓐ 2 yd   Ⓒ 10,560 yd

Ⓑ 3,520 yd   Ⓓ 28,160 yd

4. Sasha drinks 2 liters of water each weekday. She drinks 2,700 milliliters of water on Saturday and 3,300 milliliters of water on Sunday. How many milliliters of water does Sasha drink each week?

Ⓐ 0.16 mL

Ⓑ 160 mL

Ⓒ 1,600 mL

Ⓓ 16,000 mL

5. Barbara gave Debra a piece of fabric 142 centimeters long for a quilt and another piece of fabric 2 meters long for curtains. How can Debra find the total length of fabric, in centimeters, that she received from Barbara?

Ⓐ Multiply 2 by 100, then add 142.

Ⓑ Add 2 and 142, then multiply by 100.

Ⓒ Divide 142 by 100, then add 2000.

Ⓓ Multiply 2 by 2000, then add 142.

6. Cedric lives at one end of Main Street, and Landon lives at the other end of the street. Main Street is 6.02 kilometers long. Cedric walks 3.9 kilometers toward Landon's house. How many more meters must Cedric walk to arrive at Landon's house?

Ⓐ 2.12 m

Ⓑ 2120 m

Ⓒ 3920 m

Ⓓ 9920 m

assessment

1. Miggy's mother is paying her to wash the windows in their house. Miggy found directions on the Internet for making a window cleaner by mixing 4 cups of water and 1 pint of vinegar. Miggy wants to double the ingredients. How many quarts of cleaner will Miggy make?

   Ⓐ 2 qt   Ⓒ 6 qt

   Ⓑ 3 qt   Ⓓ 10 qt

2. Kelsey makes scented candles to sell at the local craft fair. Each candle contains 10 ounces of wax and 1 ounce of scent. How can Kelsey determine the number of candles she can make with 50 pounds of wax?

   Ⓐ Multiply 50 and 16, then divide by 10.

   Ⓑ Multiply 50 and 10, then divide by 16.

   Ⓒ Divide 50 by 11, then multiply by 16.

   Ⓓ Divide 50 by 16, then multiply by 10.

3. The art club is collecting colorful scraps of ribbon to create a border around a rectangular bulletin board. The bulletin board is $2\frac{1}{2}$ yards long and $1\frac{1}{2}$ yards wide. How many inches of ribbon will the art club need to create the border?

   Ⓐ 24 in   Ⓒ 146 in

   Ⓑ 96 in   Ⓓ 288 in

4. The jogging path around City Park is 2.5 kilometers long. Malik used this table to record the number of laps he jogged each day for 3 days.

   Malik's Jogging Record

Day	Laps
Monday	3
Tuesday	2
Thursday	3

   How many total meters did Malik jog during the 3 days?

   Ⓐ 20,000 m

   Ⓑ 8,000 m

   Ⓒ 2,000 m

   Ⓓ 8 m

5. For his science fair project, Michael watered his bean plants with four different amounts of water: 325 milliliters, 570 milliliters, 287 milliliters, and 608 milliliters. How would Michael express the total amount of water he used in liters?

   Ⓐ 0.179 L

   Ⓑ 1.79 L

   Ⓒ 17.9 L

   Ⓓ 1,790 L

6. Tony plans to save 20 nickels each week from his allowance. A nickel weighs 5 grams. How many kilograms of nickels will Tony save in 10 weeks?

   Answer: _____

   Explain how you found your answer.

   _____

   _____

   _____

Analysis/Analyze

1. Observe the pattern. What are the next 2 terms in the pattern?

   15 inches, $2\frac{1}{2}$ feet, 1 yard 2 feet, 120 inches, _____ , _____

   Explain how you found your answer.

   _____

   _____

Analysis/Analyze

2. The Eastland City Council is planning a Founder's Day reception. They need 50 gallons of punch to serve the 800 people who are expected to attend. The mayor's wife has a recipe that makes enough punch for 100 people. She said, "I have revised my recipe to make enough punch for 800 people." The revised recipe requires the following ingredients:

   - 32 quarts pineapple juice
   - 48 pints orange juice
   - 16 cups lemon juice
   - 14 half-gallon containers of orange or lime sherbet

   Add enough ginger ale to the ingredients above to total 50 gallons.

   How many gallons of ginger ale will be needed for this recipe? _____

Journal: Analysis/Analyze

In the Laura Ingalls Wilder book, *Little House on the Prairie*, the father's nickname for Laura is "Half-pint." What is a half-pint? Why do you think he called Laura by this name?

_____

_____

_____

_____

Conversion Crossword

Use the clues to complete the *Conversion Crossword* puzzle.

ACROSS

1. 12 inches
6. $\frac{1}{12}$ foot
8. 100 centimeters
9. 4 quarts
10. $\frac{1}{10}$ centimeter
13. 1000 milliliters
15. 60 seconds
16. $\frac{1}{2}$ quart
17. 1000 milligrams
19. 36 inches
21. 7 days

DOWN

2. $\frac{1}{16}$ pound
3. 1000 meters
4. 1000 grams
5. 10 millimeters
7. 16 ounces
11. $\frac{1}{2}$ pint
12. 4 cups
14. 2000 pounds
18. 5280 feet
20. 24 hours

Parent Activities

1. Have your child estimate how many cups of milk your family needs for one week and convert the amount to quarts and/or gallons. Let your child determine how much milk to buy at the grocery store.

2. Use a marker to mark the feet on a yardstick. Have your child measure different lengths using the yardstick and express the measure in yards, feet, and inches.

3. Gather a variety of plastic containers labeled with their customary capacity (e.g., milk or juice containers, ice cream, yogurt, or sour cream cartons). Discuss the capacity relationship between the containers. Verify by pouring water from one container to another.

Name _____

1. An entomologist measured the lengths of several insects to the nearest $\frac{1}{8}$ inch. The results are shown in this chart.

Lengths of Insects

Insect Label	Length (in inches)	Insect Label	Length (in inches)
A	$\frac{1}{2}$	F	$\frac{1}{8}$
B	$\frac{7}{8}$	G	1
C	$\frac{7}{8}$	H	$\frac{3}{4}$
D	$\frac{1}{4}$	I	$\frac{1}{2}$
E	$\frac{7}{8}$	J	$\frac{1}{4}$

Draw a line plot to display the data.

4. Mrs. Rhoades surveyed her students to determine how long it took them to complete their math homework last night. The results, in hours, are shown in the chart.

Name	Time (in hours)	Name	Time (in hours)
Madeline	1	Cheyenne	$\frac{1}{2}$
Kiley	$\frac{5}{8}$	Tia	$\frac{1}{4}$
Von	$\frac{1}{2}$	Jamaal	$\frac{7}{8}$
Luis	$\frac{1}{4}$	Will	$\frac{3}{8}$
Hector	$\frac{3}{8}$	Sam	$\frac{3}{8}$
Bethany	$\frac{1}{4}$	Flora	$\frac{1}{2}$

Use the data in the chart to create a line plot. Include an appropriate title and axis labels.

Use the line plot from question 1 to answer questions 2 and 3.

2. What is the difference between the lengths of the longest insect and the shortest insect?

Answer: _____

Use the line plot from question 4 to answer questions 5 and 6.

5. How many students studied more than 30 minutes?

Answer: _____

3. If all ten insects were lined up end-to-end, what would be the total length?

Answer: _____

6. How many students studied less than 30 minutes?

Answer: _____

Words for the Wise

axis	fraction	measure
data	line plot	number line

Hip, hip, hooray for you!

partner practice

Use the line plot to answer questions 1 – 3.

Janelle measured, to the nearest $\frac{1}{8}$ inch, objects in her bedroom. She displayed her results in this line plot.

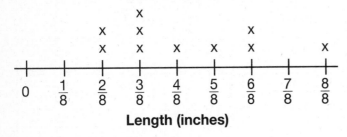

Objects Measured

Length (inches)

1. What is the total length, in inches, of the objects that are longer than $\frac{1}{2}$ inch?

   Ⓐ 1 in

   Ⓒ $3\frac{1}{8}$ in

   Ⓑ $2\frac{3}{8}$ in

   Ⓓ $4\frac{3}{4}$ in

2. How many objects have a length of $\frac{3}{4}$ inch?

   Ⓐ 3

   Ⓒ 1

   Ⓑ 2

   Ⓓ 0

3. Which shows the difference, in inches, between the lengths of the longest object and the shortest object?

   Ⓐ $\frac{7}{8}$ in

   Ⓒ $\frac{5}{8}$ in

   Ⓑ $\frac{3}{4}$ in

   Ⓓ $\frac{1}{2}$ in

Use the line plot to answer questions 4 – 6.

Raul cut a wooden dowel rod into pieces of several lengths to use in building a model for his social studies class. Raul made a line plot to show the numbers of pieces for each length that he cut.

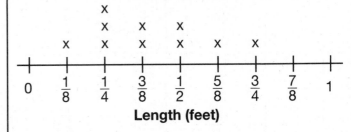

Dowel Rod Pieces

Length (feet)

4. In feet, what was the total length of the dowel rod?

   Ⓐ $4\frac{1}{2}$ ft

   Ⓒ $\frac{12}{8}$ ft

   Ⓑ 4 ft

   Ⓓ 1 ft

5. Raul used all the pieces that were less than $\frac{1}{2}$ foot long. What was the total length of the pieces Raul did **not** use?

   Ⓐ $3\frac{1}{2}$ ft

   Ⓒ $2\frac{3}{8}$ ft

   Ⓑ 3 ft

   Ⓓ $\frac{1}{2}$ ft

6. Raul had a second dowel rod that was the same length as the first rod. He cut this dowel rod into the same number of pieces as the first rod, but this time each piece was the same length. Which shows the length of each piece of the second dowel rod?

   Ⓐ $\frac{1}{3}$ ft

   Ⓒ $\frac{2}{5}$ ft

   Ⓑ $\frac{3}{8}$ ft

   Ⓓ $\frac{1}{2}$ ft

 Level 5

Use the line plot to answer questions 1 – 3.

Mr. Stamps surveyed his class to determine how much time his students spent eating dinner with their families the previous night. He displayed the results of the survey in a line plot.

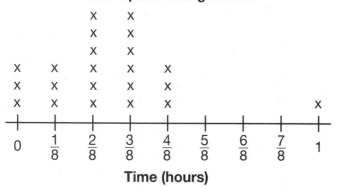

Time Spent Eating Dinner

Time (hours)

1. Which expression shows how to find the total number of hours Mr. Stamps' class spent eating dinner with their families last night?

   Ⓐ $(3 + 3 + 6 + 6 + 3 + 1) \div 60$

   Ⓑ $[(3 + 3 + 6 + 6 + 3 + 1) \times 22] \div 8$

   Ⓒ $(3 \times 0) + (3 \times \frac{1}{8}) + (6 \times \frac{1}{4}) +$
   $(6 \times \frac{3}{8}) + (3 \times \frac{1}{2}) + (1 \times \frac{8}{8})$

   Ⓓ $0 + \frac{1}{8} + \frac{1}{4} + \frac{3}{8} + \frac{1}{2} + \frac{5}{8} + \frac{3}{4} + \frac{7}{8} + 1$

2. How many students in Mr. Stamps' class spent more than $\frac{1}{2}$ hour at the dinner table last night?

   Ⓐ $\frac{1}{2}$ Ⓒ 3

   Ⓑ 1   Ⓓ 6

3. How many students did **not** eat dinner with their families last night?

   Ⓐ 0   Ⓒ 2

   Ⓑ 1   Ⓓ 3

Use the line plot to answer questions 4 – 6.

Bobbie and 7 friends worked on a math project at her home. Bobbie's younger brother, Todd, poured a carton of milk into small mugs for the girls. He poured different amounts in the mugs. The line plot shows the amounts of milk, measured in cups, that Todd poured into the mugs.

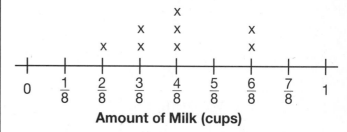

Milk Quantities

Amount of Milk (cups)

4. How many total cups of milk did Todd pour?

   Ⓐ 7 cups

   Ⓑ 5 cups

   Ⓒ 4 cups

   Ⓓ 2 cups

5. How many girls received less than $\frac{1}{2}$ cup of milk?

   Ⓐ 3

   Ⓑ 4

   Ⓒ 5

   Ⓓ 6

6. Bobbie poured milk from cup to cup to redistribute the milk equally among the mugs. How much milk did each mug contain?

   Ⓐ 1 cup

   Ⓑ $\frac{5}{8}$ cup

   Ⓒ $\frac{1}{2}$ cup

   Ⓓ $\frac{3}{8}$ cup

★ assessment

Use the line plot to answer questions 1 and 2.

After a science investigation in her classroom, Ms. Shine has 10 beakers containing different volumes of distilled water. The line plot shows the amount, in liters, of water in each beaker.

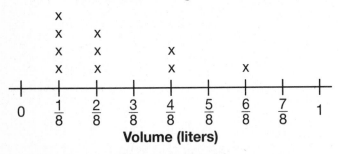

Water Remaining in Beakers

Volume (liters)

1. Which shows the total amount of water in the 10 beakers?

    Ⓐ 10 L

    Ⓑ 5 L

    Ⓒ 3 L

    Ⓓ $2\frac{3}{4}$ L

2. Ms. Shine wants to redistribute the water in the beakers so that each beaker holds the same amount. How much water will be in each beaker?

    Ⓐ $\frac{3}{10}$ L

    Ⓑ $\frac{1}{2}$ L

    Ⓒ $\frac{3}{8}$ L

    Ⓓ 1 L

Use the line plot to answer questions 3 and 4.

Mrs. Worthen planted a dozen zinnia seeds in her flower bed. The line plot shows the height of each seedling, in inches, after one week.

Heights of Zinnias

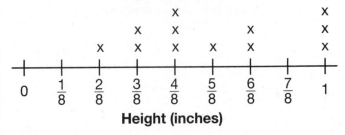

Height (inches)

3. How many zinnia seedlings had a height less than $\frac{1}{2}$ inch?

    Ⓐ 0

    Ⓑ 1

    Ⓒ 2

    Ⓓ 3

4. What is the combined height of the seedlings taller than $\frac{1}{2}$ inch?

    Ⓐ $4\frac{3}{8}$ in

    Ⓑ $5\frac{1}{8}$ in

    Ⓒ 6 in

    Ⓓ $6\frac{5}{8}$ in

5. As part of a survey, a bank asked customers what fraction of their annual income they spent on housing. The answers of the first 10 customers who took the survey are shown in the tally chart. Create a line plot to show this data.

Income Spent on Housing

Fraction Spent on Housing	Number of Responses
$\frac{1}{8}$	|||
$\frac{1}{4}$	||
$\frac{3}{8}$	||
$\frac{1}{2}$	||
$\frac{3}{4}$	|

 Level 5

Synthesis/Create

The keeper of the reptile house at the zoo measured the lengths of the snakes and recorded the data in a line plot. Write three questions that can be answered, based on the information shown in the line plot. Then, write the answer to each question.

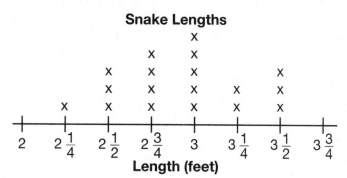

Snake Lengths

Length (feet)

Question 1: _____

_____

_____

Answer: _____

Question 2: _____

_____

_____

Answer: _____

Question 3: _____

_____

_____

Answer: _____

Journal: Analysis/Analyze

Ned said, "A number line is part of a line plot like a circle is part of a cylinder." What do you think Ned meant?

_____

_____

Name _____

Roll and Plot

Play *Roll and Plot* with a partner. Each player needs a pencil and the game board. Each pair of players needs a number cube. The object of the game is to be the first person to reach a total sum of 5 or more on his/her line plot. In turn, players roll the number cube and plot the fraction that corresponds with the number rolled. Players mark the line plot with an X to show the value of each roll while keeping a running total of points scored. The winner of the game is the player who completes the line plot first by reaching a total sum of 5 or more.

•	• •	• • •	• • • •	• • • • •	• • • • • •
$\frac{1}{8}$	$\frac{2}{8}$	$\frac{3}{8}$	$\frac{4}{8}$	$\frac{5}{8}$	$\frac{6}{8}$

$\longleftrightarrow$

| 0 | $\frac{1}{8}$ | $\frac{1}{4}$ | $\frac{3}{8}$ | $\frac{1}{2}$ | $\frac{5}{8}$ | $\frac{3}{4}$ | $\frac{7}{8}$ | $\frac{8}{8}$ |

What is the combined sum shown on your line plot?

Answer: _____

Parent Activities

1. Have your child measure, to the nearest $\frac{1}{4}$ foot, the diameter of 10 circles found around your house. Then help your child create a line plot of the data.

2. Create a deck of fraction cards on note cards, writing one fraction per card, with denominators of 2, 4, or 8. Ask your child to select at least ten fraction cards, then create a line plot to display the data.

1. Name two attributes these figures have in common.

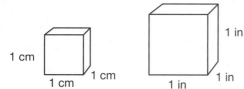

Answers:

1._____

2._____

2. U-Store-It offers a storage space shaped like this model. Each cube represents one cubic yard.

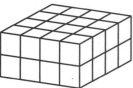

What is the volume of the storage space?

Answer: _____

3. Barry used bamboo cubes to create a plant stand in his yard, as shown in this drawing.

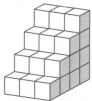

Each cube represents one cubic foot. What is the volume of Barry's plant stand?

Answer: _____

4. Thana helps her math teacher by placing foam dice into a storage box. Each die is a cube with 1-inch edges. Figure 1 shows how many dice are in the first layer Thana places in the storage box. Figure 2 shows how many layers of dice are in the storage box.

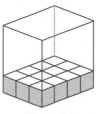 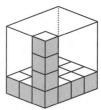

Figure 1   Figure 2

What is the volume of the storage box in cubic inches?

Answer: _____

5. Each cube in this figure is one cubic inch.

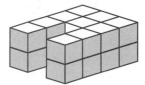

What is the volume of the figure?

Answer: _____

Words for the Wise

You're the star today!

area of base	cubic units	length
cubic centimeter (cm^3)	cubic yard (yd^3)	rectangular prism
cubic foot (ft^3)	dimension	unit cube
cubic inch (in^3)	edge	volume
cubic meter (m^3)	height	width

partner practice

1. Ebony's teacher gave her a cube with a side length of 1 inch. Which statement is **not** true about Ebony's cube?

   Ⓐ Its length, width, and height are each one inch.

   Ⓑ It can be used to help Ebony find the volume of a box.

   Ⓒ It has a volume of one inch.

   Ⓓ It is a unit cube.

2. Amber bought a necklace for her mother for Mother's Day. The necklace came in a box shaped like this model. Each cube represents one cubic inch.

   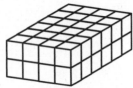

   not drawn to scale

   What is the volume of the box?

   Ⓐ 48 in³   Ⓒ 24 in³

   Ⓑ 40 in³   Ⓓ 20 in³

3. Maizie wants to display her doll collection. She uses 1-foot storage cubes to build display shelves in the corner of her bedroom as shown in this model.

   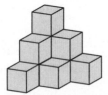

   not drawn to scale

   How many cubic feet are in Maizie's display shelves?

   Ⓐ 6 ft³   Ⓒ 9 ft³

   Ⓑ 8 ft³   Ⓓ 10 ft³

4. Wallace found a box of sugar cubes in his kitchen. He used the cubes to create a rectangular prism with a volume of 60 cubic units. Which of these drawings could **not** represent Wallace's rectangular prism?

   Ⓐ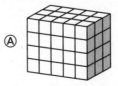

   Ⓑ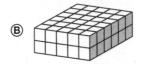

   Ⓒ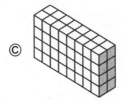

   Ⓓ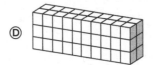

5. Jennifer packs game cubes in a packing box for shipping as shown.

   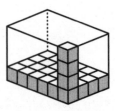

   Jennifer completely fills the box with game cubes. How many game cubes can Jennifer fit in the box?

   Ⓐ 24   Ⓒ 72

   Ⓑ 27   Ⓓ 96

1. Ian, Tess, and Cam were asked to draw a unit cube in math class. Their drawings are shown.

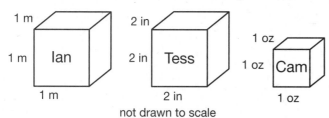

not drawn to scale

Who received credit for a correct answer?

Ⓐ Ian only

Ⓑ Cam only

Ⓒ Ian and Tess only

Ⓓ Ian and Cam only

2. Mark is shipping a gift. He needs a box that holds between 65 and 85 cubic inches. Which box could Mark use if each cube in these figures represents one cubic inch?

Ⓐ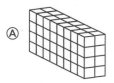

Ⓑ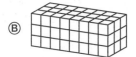

Ⓒ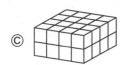

Ⓓ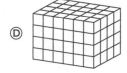

3. Hector solved a puzzle. The puzzle was a large cube made of smaller cubes, as shown in this model. Each small cube represents one cubic unit.

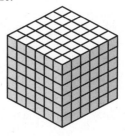

What is the volume of the puzzle?

Ⓐ 216 units³

Ⓑ 108 units³

Ⓒ 36 units³

Ⓓ 18 units³

4. Acme Appliance Center received a large carton filled with toasters in boxes, as shown in the diagram. Each toaster box in the carton has a volume of 1 cubic foot.

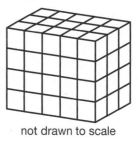

not drawn to scale

What is the volume of the large carton?

Ⓐ 400 ft³

Ⓑ 120 ft³

Ⓒ 72 ft³

Ⓓ 60 ft³

Name _____

1. Isaac made fudge for his grandfather. He cut the fudge in 1-inch cubes and began packing the fudge in a container as shown.

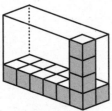

not drawn to scale

When Isaac had filled the container, how many pieces of fudge had he packed?

Ⓐ 12 Ⓒ 48

Ⓑ 17 Ⓓ 60

2. Which of these rectangular prisms does **not** have a volume of 48 cubic units?

Ⓐ   Ⓒ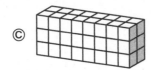

Ⓑ   Ⓓ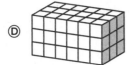

3. This model shows a rectangular prism made of 1-inch cubes.

What is the volume in cubic inches?

Ⓐ 32 in³ Ⓒ 56 in³

Ⓑ 48 in³ Ⓓ 64 in³

4. Speedy Print Shop received a shipment of paper. The warehouse manager stacked the boxes of paper as shown in the diagram. Each box has a volume of one cubic foot.

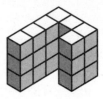

How many cubic feet of boxes are in the stack?

Ⓐ 19 ft³

Ⓑ 21 ft³

Ⓒ 22 ft³

Ⓓ 24 ft³

5. Vicki and Sasha explored measurement in the math center. The girls found the volume of a box shaped like a rectangular prism. Vicki filled the box with small cubes and then counted the cubes to find the volume. Sasha filled the box with marbles and then counted the marbles to find the volume. Which girl found the most accurate measure of the volume of the rectangular prism?

Answer: _____

Explain your answer.

_____

_____

Analysis/Analyze

1. The Mayans of Mexico and Central America built huge pyramids of solid stone blocks. Arthur built a model of a Mayan Pyramid using wooden cubes as shown. Use the figure to determine the volume, in cubic units, of Arthur's model.

Answer: _____

Explain how you found your answer.

_____

_____

_____

_____

Synthesis/Create

2. Use the dot paper to draw a geometric figure with a volume of exactly 24 cubic units.

represents 1 cubic unit

Journal: Analysis/Analyze

Unit cubes are most commonly used to determine the volume of an object. Why do you think cubes are used instead of cylinders?

_____

_____

Vie for Volume Victory

Play *Vie for Volume Victory* with the class. The teacher begins the game by signaling start. Each player finds the volumes of the shapes below and ranks them from greatest volume to least volume, with the rank of 1 noting the greatest volume and 12 noting the least volume. The winner is the first player to correctly rank the volumes of the shapes.

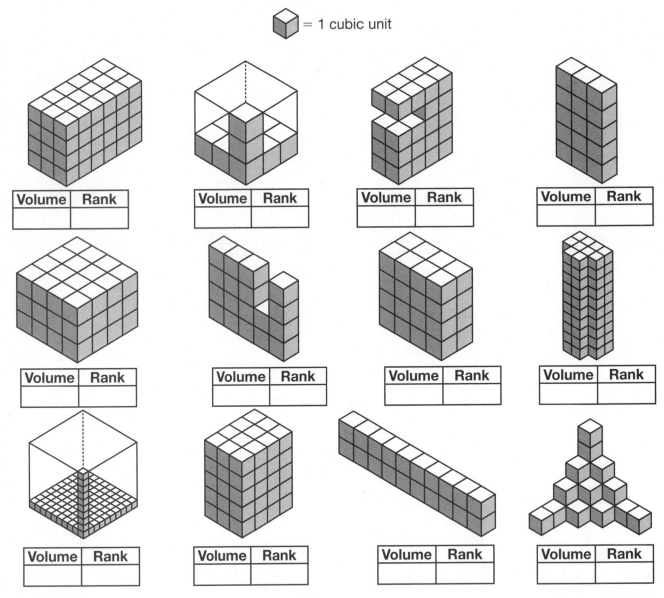

= 1 cubic unit

Volume	Rank

Volume	Rank

Volume	Rank

Volume	Rank

Volume	Rank

Volume	Rank

Volume	Rank

Volume	Rank

Volume	Rank

Volume	Rank

Volume	Rank

Volume	Rank

Parent Activities

1. Have your child use sugar cubes or 1-inch blocks to fill boxes of different sizes. Record the approximate volume of each box.

2. Talk with your child about volume. Discuss why you need to know the volume of things.

3. Have your child create a sculpture using sugar cubes. Count the cubes to determine the volume of the sculpture in cubic units.

 Level 5

1. Mickey used 1-inch cubes to create four rectangular prisms like the one shown.

not drawn to scale

Mickey stacked his cubes into a box. The cubes filled the box with no gaps or overlaps.

not drawn to scale

What is the volume, in cubic inches, of Mickey's box?

Answer: _____

2. Bert measured his cereal box with a centimeter ruler. The dimensions of the box are shown.

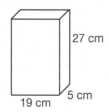

27 cm

19 cm   5 cm

What is the volume, in cubic centimeters, of the cereal box?

Answer: _____

3. A gift box with a volume of 288 cubic inches is shaped like a rectangular prism. The width of the gift box is 6 inches, and the height is 4 inches. What is the length of the gift box?

Answer: _____

Explain how you found your answer.

_____

_____

4. Mo's Bakery stacks three boxes of baked goods to create a tower of treats. The heights of the boxes are shown.

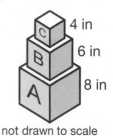

not drawn to scale

The area of the base of box A is 100 square inches. The area of the base of box B is 64 square inches, and the area of the base of box C is 36 square inches. What is the total volume of the tower of treats?

Answer: _____

Explain how you found your answer.

_____

_____

_____

Words for the Wise

Nothing to it!

area of base	cubic yard (yd³)	
cubic centimeter (cm³)	decompose	
cubic foot (ft³)	dimension	rectangular prism
cubic inch (in³)	edge	unit cube
cubic meter (m³)	height	volume
cubic unit	length	width

partner practice

1. The bottom surface of Cindy's jewelry box has an area of 65 square inches. The height of the jewelry box is 12 inches. What is the volume of Cindy's jewelry box in cubic inches?

Ⓐ 780 in³

Ⓑ 1560 in³

Ⓒ 3120 in³

Ⓓ 240 in³

2. The drawer in Marcy's writing desk is 22 inches long, 15 inches wide, and 3 inches tall. What is the volume of the drawer in cubic inches?

Ⓐ 40 in³

Ⓑ 330 in³

Ⓒ 333 in³

Ⓓ 990 in³

3. A box that holds 12 cans of soda is 16 inches long, 5 inches wide, and 5 inches tall. Which two expressions can be used to find the volume of the box in cubic inches?

Ⓐ (12 × 16) × 5 and 12 × (16 × 5)

Ⓑ (16 × 5) × 5 and 16 × (5 × 5)

Ⓒ (16 + 5) + 5 and 16 + (5 + 5)

Ⓓ (12 × 16) + 5 and 12 × (16 + 5)

4. Miranda packs glass vases in small cube-shaped boxes with edges that measure 1 foot. She then packs the cubes into larger crates. The dimensions of the base of a large crate are shown here.

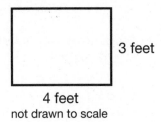

3 feet

4 feet

not drawn to scale

Miranda can pack 24 vases into a large crate, with no gaps or overlaps. How tall is a large crate, in feet?

Ⓐ 2 ft

Ⓑ 3 ft

Ⓒ 12 ft

Ⓓ 14 ft

5. Henry used 1-centimeter cubes to create a model of a science museum and planetarium. How many total cubes did Henry use in the model?

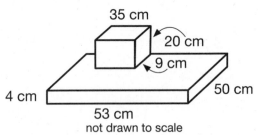

35 cm

20 cm

9 cm

4 cm

50 cm

53 cm

not drawn to scale

Ⓐ 8,100

Ⓑ 13,300

Ⓒ 16,900

Ⓓ 22,050

Level 5

Name _____

1. Aunt Posey packs jars of homemade salsa in small, cube-shaped boxes. Then she stacks several layers of small boxes into a larger packing box. One layer of small boxes is shown here.

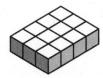

Aunt Posey's large packing box has a volume of 60 cubic units. The small boxes completely fill the large box, with no gaps or overlaps. Each small box of salsa represents one cubic unit. How many layers of small boxes does Aunt Posey pack into a large box?

Ⓐ 4   Ⓒ 12

Ⓑ 5   Ⓓ 720

2. The children's play pool at the park has a rectangular base with an area of 144 square feet. The play pool is 2 feet deep. What is the volume of the pool in cubic feet?

Ⓐ 144 ft³   Ⓒ 576 ft³

Ⓑ 288 ft³   Ⓓ 1152 ft³

3. The base of a cube with 3-meter edges is shown here.

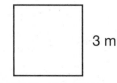

3 m

not drawn to scale

Which equation can be used to find the volume of the cube, in cubic meters?

Ⓐ 3 × 3 = 9   Ⓒ 9 × 3 = 27

Ⓑ 3 × 4 = 12   Ⓓ 9 × 6 = 54

4. Which of these boxes does **not** have a volume of 240 cubic centimeters?

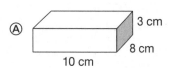
Ⓐ   3 cm   8 cm   10 cm

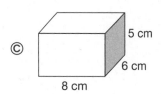
Ⓑ   4 cm   6 cm   10 cm

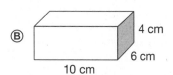
Ⓒ   5 cm   6 cm   8 cm

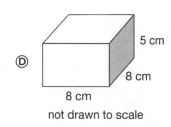
Ⓓ   5 cm   8 cm   8 cm

not drawn to scale

5. Tara connected two pieces of wood to form her initial, as shown in the model. What was the volume of the wood Tara used, in cubic inches?

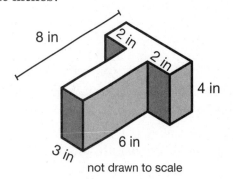

8 in   2 in   2 in   4 in   3 in   6 in

not drawn to scale

Ⓐ 72 in³   Ⓒ 128 in³

Ⓑ 96 in³   Ⓓ 146 in³

assessment

1. Lucy's younger brother plays with wooden blocks that are 1-inch cubes. Lucy picks up her brother's blocks and stacks them in this box. The volume of the box is 490 cubic inches. The blocks fit into the box without gaps or overlaps. How tall is the box?

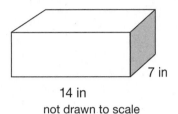

14 in

not drawn to scale

Ⓐ 5 in

Ⓑ 6 in

Ⓒ 98 in

Ⓓ 392 in

2. Tim made a tissue box. The area of the base is 45 square inches. The height of the box is 4 inches. What is the volume of the tissue box?

Ⓐ 90 in³

Ⓑ 180 in³

Ⓒ 360 in³

Ⓓ 1080 in³

3. Mrs. Ali is packing clothes in this storage box.

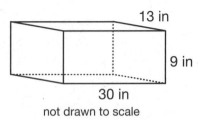

not drawn to scale

Which two expressions could Mrs. Ali use to find the volume of the box in cubic inches?

Ⓐ $(30 \times 13) \times (13 \times 9)$ and $30 \times (9 \times 13)$

Ⓑ $(30 \times 9) \times 13$ and $(30 \times 13) + (30 \times 9)$

Ⓒ $30 \times (9 \times 13)$ and $(30 \times 9) \times 13$

Ⓓ $30 \times (9 + 13)$ and $(30 + 9) \times 13$

4. Mr. Robb built concrete steps for a storage building as shown. How many cubic inches of concrete did Mr. Robb use?

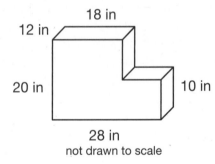

not drawn to scale

Ⓐ 4,600 in³   Ⓒ 6,720 in³

Ⓑ 5,520 in³   Ⓓ 10,320 in³

5. Old Town Bakery packages their fudge cakes in boxes. Each box has a volume of 600 cubic inches. The height of the box is 6 inches as shown.

What could be the length and width of the box?

Answer: _____

Justify your answer.

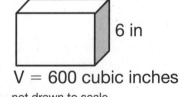

V = 600 cubic inches

not drawn to scale

_____

_____

Analysis/Analyze ——————————————————————————————

1. Mrs. Roberts packed a box of decorations to store in her attic. She started with a box shaped like a cube that measured 2 feet on each side. She discovered that this box was too small. She repacked the decorations into a larger box, also shaped like a cube. The volume of the larger box was 8 times the volume of the first box. How long were the sides on the larger box?

Answer: _____

Explain how you found your answer. _____

_____

_____

_____

Analysis/Analyze ——————————————————————————————

2. Ross created this design.

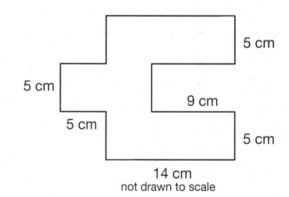

Ross stacked several layers of 1-centimeter cubes on his design, until he had used exactly 760 cubes. How many layers of cubes did Ross stack?

Answer: _____

Explain how you found your answer.

_____

_____

_____

Journal: Analysis/Analyze ——————————————————

Explain why area is measured in square units and volume is measured in cubic units.

_____

_____

_____

★ **motivation station**

Volume Match

Play *Volume Match* with a partner. The object of the game is to connect each prism to its matching volume. In turn, players find the volume of one prism and draw a path to the answer. If a player selects a prism with no matching volume or if a player finds an incorrect volume, he/she loses that turn. The winner is the player with the most correct matches.

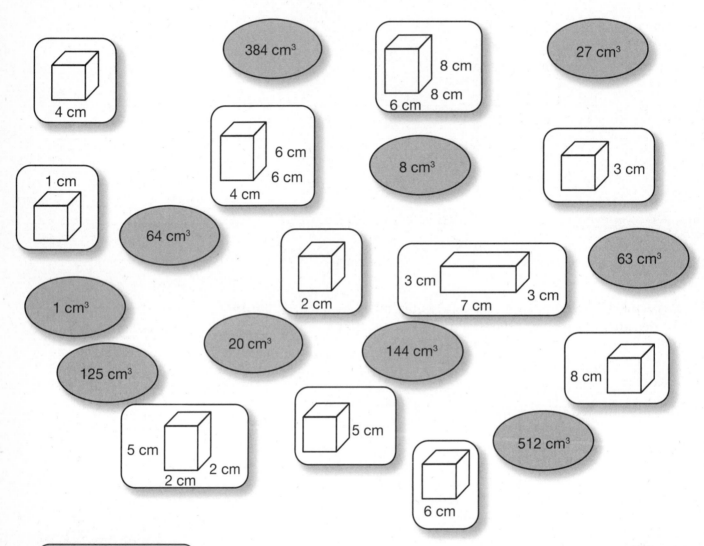

Parent Activities

1. Use catalogs to find large appliances. Point out that these items arrive at stores in boxes or crates. Have your child use the approximate dimensions (to the nearest foot) to estimate the volumes of the boxes or crates in which the items were shipped.

2. Have your child use 1-inch blocks to build rectangular prisms of various sizes. Multiply the dimensions of the prisms to find the volume in cubic inches. Then deconstruct the prisms, count the cubes, and compare to the calculated volume.

3. Have your child use a ruler, tape measure, or yardstick to measure the dimensions of a variety of household items to the nearest inch or foot. Estimate the volume of a box that would be large enough to hold each item.

 Level 5

Name _____

1. Marissa plotted five points on a coordinate grid.

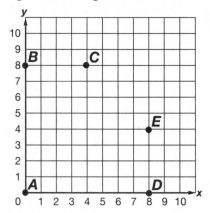

Which point is located at the origin? _____

What are the coordinates of point *B*? _____

Which point is located at (4, 8)? _____

Points *A*, *B*, *C*, and *D* form the vertices of a polygon. What polygon is formed? _____

2. Which labeled point is located inside the circle but outside the square? _____

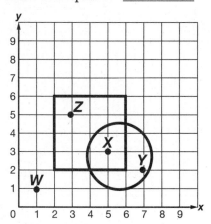

What are the coordinates of this point?

Answer: _____

3. Name three ordered pairs that are located on the letter L shown on this coordinate plane.

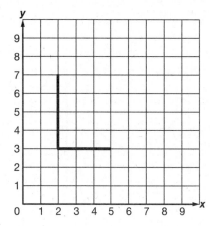

Answer: _____

4. Plot these points. Draw a line segment to connect each pair.

(2,2) and (2,9)

(9,2) and (9,9)

(2,6) and (9,6)

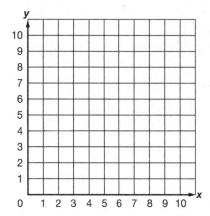

What letter is formed on the grid?

Answer: _____

Words for the Wise

You make this look easy!

axis/axes	origin	vertical
coordinate plane	parallel	*x*-axis
coordinates	perpendicular	*x*-coordinate
horizontal	plot	*y*-axis
ordered pair	point	*y*-coordinate

partner practice

Use the graph to answer questions 1 – 3.

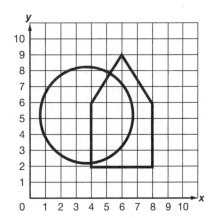

1. Which ordered pair represents a point located inside both the circle and the pentagon?

   Ⓐ (5, 7)   　　Ⓒ (3, 6)

   Ⓑ (7, 5)   　　Ⓓ (6, 3)

2. Which ordered pair represents a point that is **not** located on the perimeter of the pentagon?

   Ⓐ (6, 9)   　　Ⓒ (6, 4)

   Ⓑ (4, 6)   　　Ⓓ (8, 6)

3. Which ordered pair represents a point that is located in the circle but is **not** in the pentagon?

   Ⓐ (5, 5)   　　Ⓒ (7, 3)

   Ⓑ (3, 7)   　　Ⓓ (0, 0)

4. In which of the following groups of ordered pairs is each point located on the letter T shown on this coordinate plane?

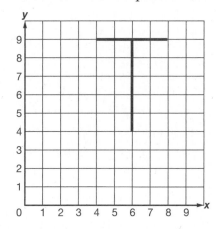

   Ⓐ (6, 6), (6, 9), (5, 3)

   Ⓑ (6, 5), (5, 9), (7, 9)

   Ⓒ (6, 3), (1, 6), (3, 3)

   Ⓓ (7, 5), (4, 8), (3, 2)

5. Four points are labeled on this graph.

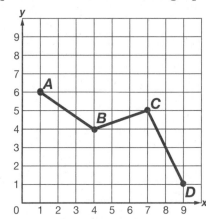

Which table shows the coordinates of the labeled points on the graph?

Ⓐ
x	y
1	6
3	3
7	4
9	2

Ⓒ
x	y
1	6
4	4
7	5
9	1

Ⓑ
x	y
6	1
4	4
5	7
1	9

Ⓓ
x	y
1	1
4	2
4	3
9	1

     Level 5

Use the graph to answer questions 1 – 3.

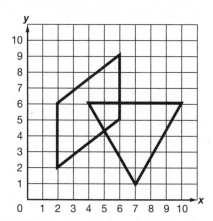

1. Which ordered pair represents a point located inside both the parallelogram and the triangle?

   Ⓐ (5, 4)   Ⓒ (5, 5)

   Ⓑ (4, 5)   Ⓓ (4, 4)

2. Which ordered pair represents a point that is **not** located on the perimeter of the parallelogram?

   Ⓐ (7, 6)   Ⓒ (2, 6)

   Ⓑ (6, 7)   Ⓓ (6, 6)

3. Which ordered pair represents a point that is located inside the triangle but is **not** inside the parallelogram?

   Ⓐ (5, 8)   Ⓒ (8, 5)

   Ⓑ (5, 5)   Ⓓ (3, 5)

4. Which of the following groups of ordered pairs are located on the perimeter of this triangle?

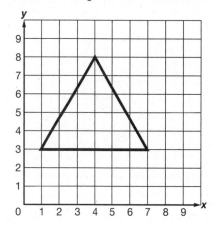

   Ⓐ (2, 3), (4, 8), (5, 3)

   Ⓑ (4, 5), (2, 8), (3, 5)

   Ⓒ (2, 3), (1, 6), (3, 3)

   Ⓓ (6, 3), (2, 4), (7, 6)

5. Prim draws a line segment from (2, 4) to (5, 1). She wants to draw another line segment parallel to her line segment. Which two coordinates would **not** form a line segment parallel to Prim's line segment?

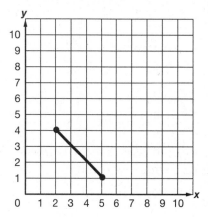

   Ⓐ (1, 7), (4, 4)   Ⓒ (6, 3), (10, 2)

   Ⓑ (5, 7), (8, 4)   Ⓓ (8, 9), (10, 7)

Use the graph to answer questions 1 – 3.

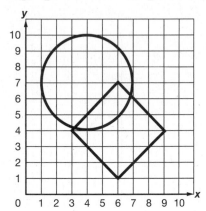

1. Which ordered pair represents a point located inside both the circle and the square?

Ⓐ (3, 5)   Ⓒ (5, 5)

Ⓑ (5, 3)   Ⓓ (3, 3)

2. Which ordered pairs are located on the vertices of the square?

Ⓐ (1, 6), (4, 3), (7, 6), (4, 9)

Ⓑ (3, 4), (6, 7), (9, 4), (6, 1)

Ⓒ (5, 6), (8, 5), (7, 2), (5, 2)

Ⓓ (1, 7), (4, 10), (7, 7), (4, 4)

3. Which ordered pair is located inside the circle but is **not** inside the square?

Ⓐ (6, 3)   Ⓒ (7, 5)

Ⓑ (1, 4)   Ⓓ (4, 7)

4. Which table shows the coordinates of the labeled points on the graph?

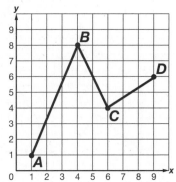

Ⓐ
x	y
1	1
8	4
5	2
9	6

Ⓒ
x	y
1	1
4	8
4	6
6	9

Ⓑ
x	y
1	1
4	8
6	4
9	6

Ⓓ
x	y
1	1
3	4
6	4
9	1

5. Plot these points on the coordinate plane.

Point *J*: (3, 3)

Point *K*: (7, 8)

Point *L*: (7, 3)

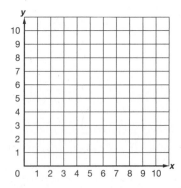

Draw line segments to connect the points in order. Also draw a line segment from Point *L* to Point *J*.

What geometric figure is formed?

Answer: _____

Synthesis/Create

1. Create a sentence by forming words from the letters shown in the coordinate grid. Give the coordinates of each letter used to make the sentence.

   Example: Have a great day = (4,3) (4,1) (8,9) (5,4)
   (2,4) (1,6) (4,9) (7,1) (1,4) (8,7) (6,3) (3,6) (1,2)

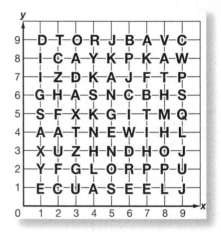

_____

_____

_____

_____

Analysis/Analyze

2. Are the coordinates (5, 6) the same as the coordinates (6, 5)? Explain your answer with pictures and words.

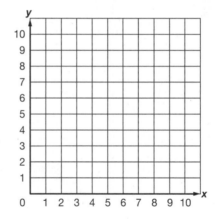

_____

_____

Journal: Analysis/Analyze

Explain a way to help students remember how to plot an ordered pair on the coordinate plane.

_____

_____

_____

★ motivation station

Find the Treasure

Play *Find the Treasure* with a partner. Each player needs a pencil and the game board. Each pair of players needs a number cube. In turn, a player rolls the number cube and writes the number rolled in the first column of the table, then rolls again and writes the number in the second column of the table. The player uses the coordinates to locate the points on the grid and uses an X to mark the spot. The winner is the first player to mark an X on all of the treasure chests or the player who has the most treasure chests marked after 20 turns.

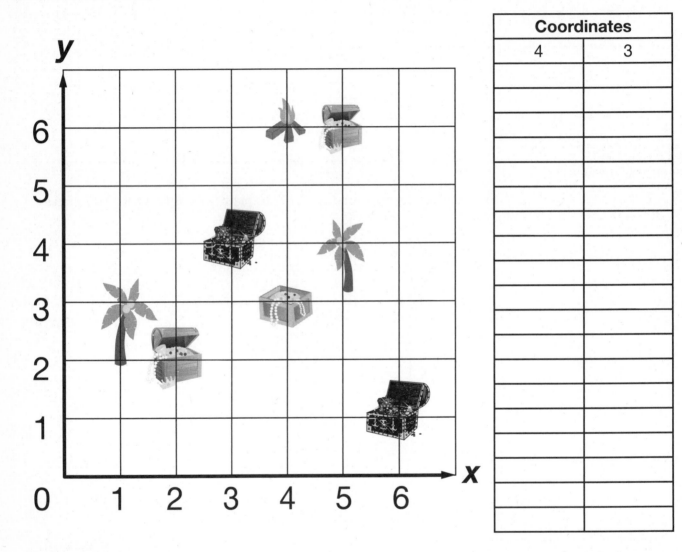

Coordinates	
4	3

Parent Activities

1. Play coordinate grid Tic-Tac-Toe. Use 2 dice, one for the *x*-axis (horizontal number line) and the other for the *y*-axis (vertical number line). Plot the numbers you roll on a sheet of grid paper. Try to get 3 plots in a row.

2. Play the same Tic-Tac-Toe game, but use playing cards. Divide the playing cards by color. The black cards represent the *x*-axis, and the red cards represent the *y*-axis. Turn over one of each color and plot on a sheet of grid paper.

 Level 5

Name _____

1. The coordinate grid shows the location of booths at the school carnival.

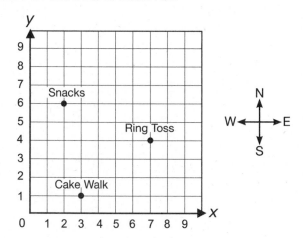

Coach Jones is placing a Dunking Booth that is not shown on the grid. The Dunking Booth is 4 units north of the Ring Toss. What are the coordinates of the Dunking Booth?

Answer: _____

2. For several hours during a spring rainfall, Amanda recorded the level of water in her rain gauge. She used her data to create this graph.

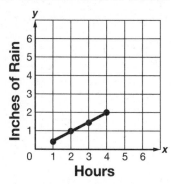

Rain continued to fall at the same rate. How much rain fell in 6 hours?

Answer: _____

3. Paul plotted three vertices of a parallelogram on this coordinate plane.

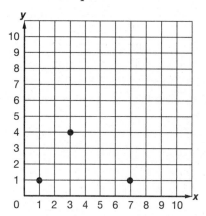

Name the coordinates of the missing vertex.

Answer: _____

4. At Hancock's Hardware, the cost of 1 light bulb is $2. Complete the table to show how much 2 light bulbs, 3 light bulbs, and 4 light bulbs will cost. Then graph the ordered pairs on the coordinate plane.

Number of bulbs (x)	Cost in dollars (y)
1	2
2	
3	
4	

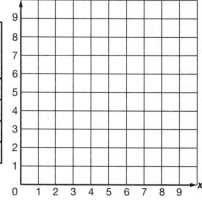

Words for the Wise

Make this your personal best!

axis/axes	origin	
coordinate plane	plot	
coordinates	point	x-coordinate
horizontal	vertical	y-axis
ordered pair	x-axis	y-coordinate

partner practice

1. Look at the map of Yim's neighborhood on this coordinate plane.

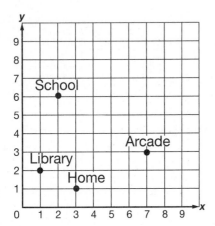

Yim is standing at $(6, 4)$. He is closest to which of the following points?

Ⓐ School Ⓒ Home

Ⓑ Library Ⓓ Arcade

2. Rina plotted two vertices of an isosceles triangle on this coordinate plane.

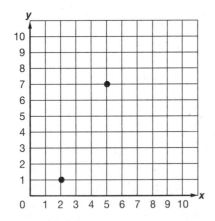

Which could be the coordinates of the missing vertex of Rina's triangle?

Ⓐ $(1, 8)$ Ⓒ $(8, 1)$

Ⓑ $(5, 1)$ Ⓓ $(7, 4)$

3. Kelly created a graph showing how many pints are equal to a given number of quarts.

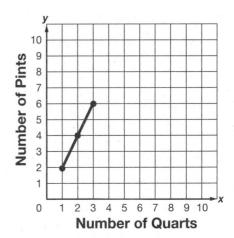

Based on Kelly's graph, which ordered pair represents the number of pints equal to 5 quarts?

Ⓐ $(10, 5)$ Ⓒ $(5, 8)$

Ⓑ $(8, 5)$ Ⓓ $(5, 10)$

4. This grid can be used to represent Marina's neighborhood.

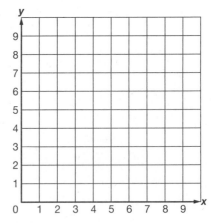

Marina's house is located at $(3, 5)$. She walks 4 units to the right and 3 units down to the library. Which ordered pair represents the location of the library?

Ⓐ $(7, 5)$ Ⓒ $(2, 7)$

Ⓑ $(7, 2)$ Ⓓ $(5, 7)$

 Level 5

Use the coordinate plane to answer questions 1 – 3.

Karl made this grid to show the locations of some things on the playground.

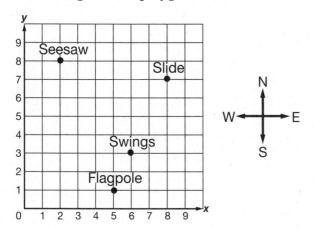

1. Which ordered pair represents the point on the grid labeled "Swings"?

   Ⓐ (3, 6)   Ⓒ (5, 0)

   Ⓑ (8, 7)   Ⓓ (6, 3)

2. One possible path from the slide to the seesaw is

   Ⓐ walk north one square, then east 6 squares.

   Ⓑ walk west 6 squares, then south 1 square.

   Ⓒ walk west 6 squares, then north 1 square.

   Ⓓ walk west 1 square, then north 6 squares.

3. The Cub Scouts want to plant a tree for Arbor Day. They decide to plant the tree three squares west and two squares north of the flagpole. What will be the coordinates of the tree?

   Ⓐ (8, 3)   Ⓒ (3, 8)

   Ⓑ (2, 3)   Ⓓ (3, 2)

Use the coordinate plane to answer questions 4 – 6.

Brad makes a profit of $3 on each fishing lure he makes. This graph shows his profit for selling 1, 2, or 3 lures.

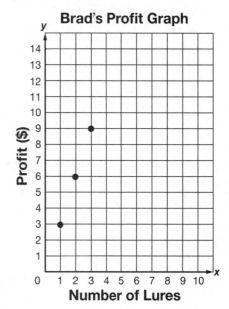

4. How much profit does Brad make if he sells 3 fishing lures?

   Ⓐ $3   Ⓒ $9

   Ⓑ $6   Ⓓ $12

5. Which ordered pair would Brad plot to show the profit for selling 5 lures?

   Ⓐ (5, 15)   Ⓒ (15, 5)

   Ⓑ (5, 10)   Ⓓ (10, 5)

6. Which **best** describes the meaning of the point at the origin of Brad's graph?

   Ⓐ If Brad sells 0 lures, he makes $3 in profit.

   Ⓑ If Brad sells 1 lure, he makes $3 in profit.

   Ⓒ If Brad sells 10 lures, he makes $30 in profit.

   Ⓓ If Brad sells no lures, he receives no profit.

★ **assessment**

1. Rondall works during the summer mowing lawns. He plans to save the same amount of money each week. The graph shows Rondall's savings over several weeks.

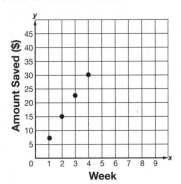

How much money will Rondall have saved after working exactly 6 weeks?

Ⓐ $30 Ⓒ $45

Ⓑ $40 Ⓓ $50

2. Shirley plotted three vertices of an isosceles trapezoid on a coordinate plane.

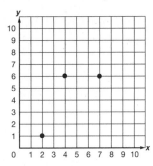

Which could be the coordinates of the missing vertex of Shirley's trapezoid?

Ⓐ (10, 0) Ⓒ (7, 1)

Ⓑ (9, 1) Ⓓ (1, 9)

Use the coordinate plane to answer questions 3 and 4.

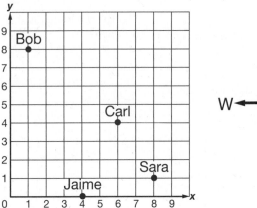

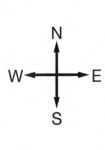

3. Rich's house is located at (2, 7). Whose house is closest to Rich's house?

Ⓐ Sara's Ⓒ Jamie's

Ⓑ Bob's Ⓓ Carl's

4. Mike, whose house is **not** shown on the grid, lives 2 units east and 5 units north of Carl. What are the coordinates of Mike's house?

Ⓐ (4, 9) Ⓒ (4, 6)

Ⓑ (6, 4) Ⓓ (8, 9)

5. Marissa runs every day on a path around the pond at the City Park. She starts at point S, runs to point T, then runs to point U and back to point S.

What are the ordered pairs that represent the 3 vertices of the triangle that Marisa runs?

Answer: *S:* _____ *T:* _____ *U:* _____

Name an ordered pair that represents a point in the pond.

Answer: _____

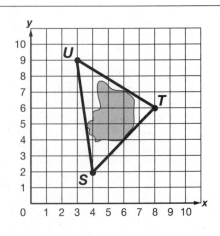

Analysis/Analyze

Four friends are going to the Skateplex. Use the clues to locate each friend's house and the Skateplex on the coordinate plane.

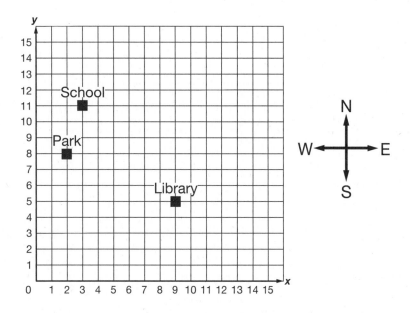

- The quickest way to get to Tomiko's house is to travel one block east from the park and then travel five blocks south.
- Lupe lives exactly two blocks east of the library and seven blocks south of the Skateplex.
- Daniel only has to walk four blocks west to get to school each day.
- The first coordinate for Patrick's house is 9 greater than the first coordinate for Tomiko's house; the second coordinate for Patrick's house is the same as the second coordinate for Tomiko's house.

What are the coordinates for each friend's house?

Tomiko: (____ , ____)   Daniel: (____ , ____)

Lupe: (____ , ____)   Patrick: (____ , ____)

What are the coordinates for the Skateplex? (____ , ____)

Whose house is closest to the Skateplex? _____

Journal: Analysis/Analyze

Explain how coordinate grids are used in the real world.

_____

_____

_____

Name _____

Map It

Create a map of Shady Glen School on the coordinate grid. Include the places shown on the map key. Use your map to answer the questions about ordered pairs.

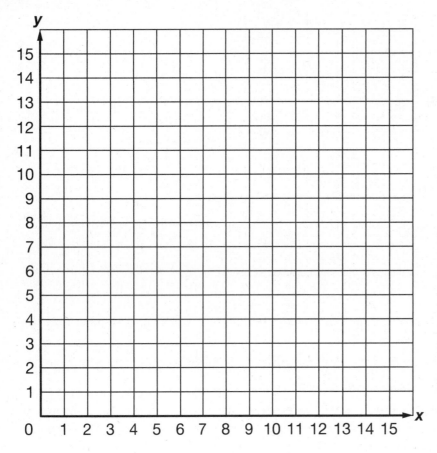

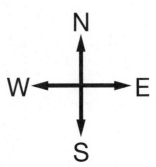

Map Key

C = Cafeteria
P = Playground
L = Library
G = Gym
O = Office
N = Nurse

Use ordered pairs and the compass rose to explain how to get from the office to the cafeteria.

_____

_____

Which locations on the school map are the farthest apart? Use evidence from the ordered pair coordinates to support your answer.

_____

Parent Activities

1. Using an atlas or road map, have your child locate specific cities or landmarks using coordinates. Discuss how the coordinates on a map are similar to ordered pairs on a coordinate plane.

2. Play games such as Battleship in which children use ordered pairs on a coordinate grid. Note that some interactive versions of Battleship are available online.

 Level 5

Name _____

1. Draw 3 different right triangles. Place an X on the right angle.

2. In a regular polygon, all sides and all angles are congruent. Sketch a regular pentagon.

3. Sketch a regular octagon and an octagon that is not regular.

   Name two ways the octagons are different.

   _____

   _____

4. Name two figures that are parallelograms.

   Answer: _____

   Name two figures that are **not** parallelograms.

   Answer: _____

   Explain why the two non-examples are **not** parallelograms.

   _____

   _____

   _____

5. Is it possible to create an equilateral triangle that has a right angle? Justify your answer.

   Answer: _____

   _____

   _____

6. Do all parallelograms have right angles? Explain your answer with words and pictures.

   Answer: _____

   _____

   _____

Words for the Wise

angle	perpendicular	
attribute	polygon	right angle
circle	quadrilateral	right triangle
congruent	rectangle	square
parallel	regular polygon	triangle
parallelogram	rhombus	two-dimensional figure

A success... THATS YOU!

partner practice

1. Which statement is **not** true about a square?

Ⓐ This figure is a rectangle.

Ⓑ This figure is a parallelogram.

Ⓒ This figure is a rhombus.

Ⓓ This figure is a trapezoid.

2. Gretchen is drawing different shapes to create a mosaic. She decides to measure the triangle in the middle of the mosaic. All three side lengths have different measures. Which type of triangle is located in the center of Gretchen's mosaic?

Ⓐ isosceles

Ⓑ equilateral

Ⓒ scalene

Ⓓ regular

3. Mya is creating a Venn diagram to display quadrilaterals that are parallelograms. Which of the following is **not** considered a parallelogram?

Ⓐ rhombus

Ⓑ rectangle

Ⓒ square

Ⓓ trapezoid

4. Kylesha is coloring a design made of regular hexagons. Which of the following is **not** true about a regular hexagon?

Ⓐ All six sides have the same length.

Ⓑ All six angles are congruent.

Ⓒ There are six right angles.

Ⓓ There are six lines of symmetry.

5. Which shows a set of figures that possesses all these attributes?

• Opposite angles are congruent.
• Opposite sides are parallel.
• They contain four right angles.

Ⓐ rectangles and trapezoids

Ⓑ rectangles and squares

Ⓒ isosceles triangles and equilateral triangles

Ⓓ quadrilaterals and trapezoids

6. Which does **not** appear to be a classification of the figure shown?

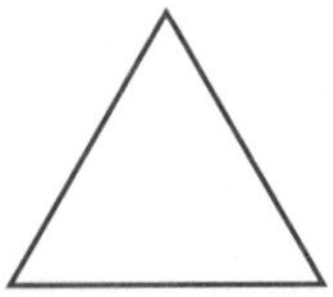

Ⓐ an acute triangle

Ⓑ a regular polygon

Ⓒ an equilateral triangle

Ⓓ a scalene triangle

 Level 5

Name _____

1. Mr. Jimmerson drew this figure.

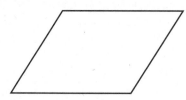

Which statement does **not** appear to be true about the figure?

Ⓐ The figure is a parallelogram.

Ⓑ The figure is a polygon.

Ⓒ The figure is a quadrilateral.

Ⓓ The figure is a rhombus.

2. Samuel's math teacher assigned a geometric figure to each group of students. Samuel's group was given an isosceles triangle. The group discussed the attributes of isosceles triangles. Which of the following statements is true about isosceles triangles?

Ⓐ All three angles will always be acute.

Ⓑ All isosceles triangles have one obtuse angle.

Ⓒ All isosceles triangles have at least two congruent sides.

Ⓓ An isosceles triangle can never include a right angle.

3. Roger compared the properties of several quadrilaterals. He noticed that a quadrilateral with all the properties of a rhombus and all the properties of a rectangle would best be described as a

Ⓐ square.   Ⓒ parallelogram.

Ⓑ trapezoid.   Ⓓ quadrilateral.

4. Saul knows that an irregular polygon is a polygon in which the sides and the angles are not all congruent. Based on this definition, which of the following is **always** an irregular polygon?

Ⓐ rectangle   Ⓒ quadrilateral

Ⓑ rhombus   Ⓓ trapezoid

5. Sullivan is listing the attributes of a parallelogram as part of his homework assignment. Which of the following attributes does **not** describe a parallelogram?

Ⓐ All parallelograms have opposite angles that are congruent.

Ⓑ All parallelograms have opposite sides that are congruent.

Ⓒ All parallelograms have four sides.

Ⓓ All parallelograms have four angles that measure 90°.

6. Nancy knows that an acute triangle has three acute angles. She knows that an obtuse triangle has exactly one obtuse angle. Based on these facts, which statement below **must** be true?

Ⓐ Every acute triangle is also an obtuse triangle.

Ⓑ Every obtuse triangle is also an acute triangle.

Ⓒ A triangle cannot be both acute and obtuse.

Ⓓ All triangles are acute triangles.

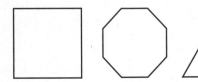

1. These pictures are examples of regular polygons.

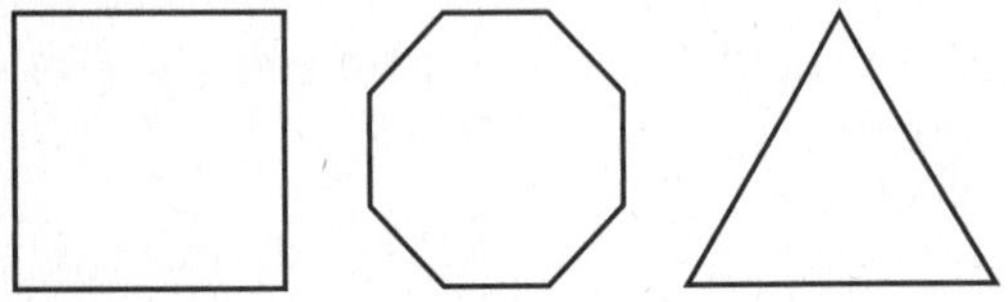

What conclusion can be drawn about all regular polygons?

Ⓐ Every regular polygon has 90° angles.

Ⓑ All regular polygons have an even number of sides.

Ⓒ A regular polygon has sides that are congruent.

Ⓓ All regular polygons have acute angles.

2. Conner recalls that an equilateral triangle has three congruent angles that are acute. Which shows another attribute of equilateral triangles?

Ⓐ Exactly two sides are congruent.

Ⓑ All three sides are congruent.

Ⓒ One side length has the same measurement as the angles.

Ⓓ There is only one line of symmetry.

3. Geneva chose to study quadrilaterals for her math project. She discovered that parallelograms have two pairs of parallel sides. Which figure is **not** a parallelogram?

Ⓐ trapezoid

Ⓑ rectangle

Ⓒ square

Ⓓ rhombus

4. Mrs. Watson gave her students several different triangles and asked them to group the triangles according to their angle measures. One group was acute triangles. Which statement is true about all acute triangles?

Ⓐ All acute triangles have 3 acute angles.

Ⓑ All acute triangles have 3 acute angles that are congruent.

Ⓒ All acute triangles have 3 congruent sides.

Ⓓ All acute triangles have 3 angles that measure more than 90°.

5. Place a check mark before all the possible classifications for the figure shown. Then write a sentence justifying each checked classification.

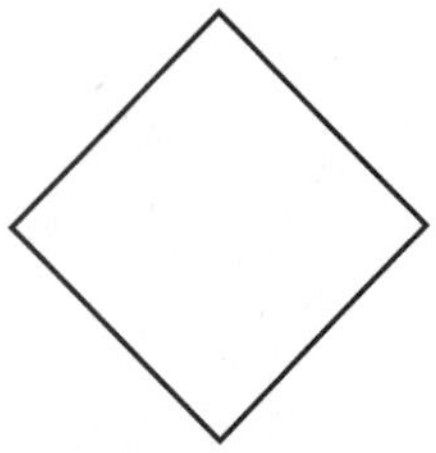

___Polygon_____

___Quadrilateral _____

___Parallelogram _____

___Rectangle _____

___Rhombus _____

Analysis/Analyze

1. Research the prefixes of each word shown in the table. Complete the table by writing the meaning of each prefix, and then give examples of two other words that begin with the prefix.

Prefix	Geometric shape with Prefix	Meaning of Prefix	Other Words that Begin with Prefix
poly-	polygon		
hex-	hexagon		
quad-	quadrilateral		
tri-	triangle		
pent-	pentagon		
oct-	octagon		

Synthesis/Create

2. Create a picture made **only** of figures that have at least one right angle.

Journal: Analysis/Analyze

Explain why all squares are rectangles but not all rectangles are squares.

_____

_____

_____

★ motivation station

Polygon Pursuit

Ernie drew a square and then drew some line segments in the square as shown.

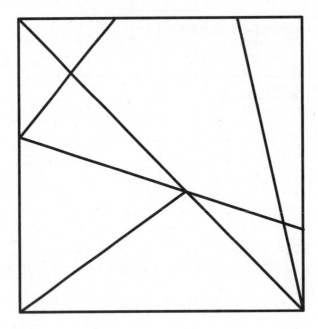

Using different colors of markers or pencils, trace and name at least 4 different polygons you can find in Ernie's figure.

_____

_____

_____

_____

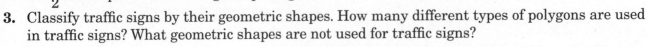

Parent Activities

1. Take your child on a geometric scavenger hunt. Search your house, yard, or the park for real-world objects that are shaped like triangles or quadrilaterals (four-sided figures). Have your child draw each object. Once he/she has found 10 or more items, sort the items by characteristics. For example, make a group of quadrilaterals that have all right angles or a group of triangles in which all 3 side lengths are the same.

2. Ask your child to draw specific 2-dimensional figures using a ruler, pencil, and paper (e.g., Draw a $4\frac{1}{2}$-inch square. Draw a regular pentagon.).

3. Classify traffic signs by their geometric shapes. How many different types of polygons are used in traffic signs? What geometric shapes are not used for traffic signs?

Use the hierarchy diagram for questions 1 – 5.

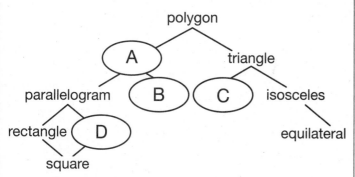

1. Marisol must complete the hierarchy diagram for a geometry assignment. In Oval D, Marisol wrote "quadrilateral." Is Marisol correct?

   Answer: _____

   Justify your answer._____

   _____

   _____

2. Marisol correctly placed the word "trapezoid" in the diagram. What is the letter in the oval where Marisol wrote "trapezoid"?

   Answer: _____

   Justify your answer._____

   _____

   _____

3. Marisol read these three definitions in her math glossary.

   > **scalene triangle** – a triangle with no congruent sides
   >
   > **isosceles triangle** – a triangle with at least two congruent sides
   >
   > **equilateral triangle** – a triangle with exactly 3 congruent sides and 3 congruent acute angles

   She wants to write one of these triangle names in Oval C. Which triangle name should Marisol choose?

   Answer: _____

4. Based on her completed hierarchy diagram, Marisol makes this statement:

   > Every rectangle has two pairs of congruent sides and two pairs of parallel sides.

   Is Marisol's statement correct?

   Answer: _____

5. Marisol draws a polygon with four congruent sides and two pairs of parallel sides. She also notices that two angles are acute and two angles are obtuse. What word **best** describes Marisol's polygon?

   Answer: _____

Words for the Wise

Stay on the fast track!

acute angle	kite	
acute triangle	obtuse angle	rhombus
adjacent	obtuse triangle	right angle
attribute	parallel lines	right triangle
congruent	perpendicular lines	scalene triangle
equilateral triangle	polygon	square
hierarchy	quadrilateral	trapezoid
isosceles triangle	rectangle	triangle

★ partner practice

Use the hierarchy diagram to answer questions 1 – 3.

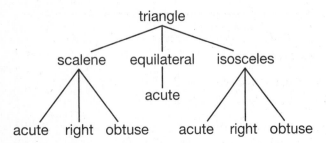

1. According to the diagram, which of these statements is **not** true?

    Ⓐ Every acute triangle has 3 congruent sides.

    Ⓑ An obtuse triangle can have 2 congruent sides.

    Ⓒ A right triangle cannot have 3 congruent sides.

    Ⓓ An obtuse triangle can also be scalene.

2. Juan used a ruler and determined that the sides of a triangle measured 5 centimeters, 12 centimeters, and 13 centimeters. Then he used a protractor to find that the triangle had one 90° angle and two angles that were each less than 90°. Which **best** describes the triangle Juan measured?

    Ⓐ isosceles right

    Ⓒ scalene right

    Ⓑ acute scalene

    Ⓓ acute equilateral

3. Based on the diagram, which of the following statements is true?

    Ⓐ An isosceles triangle cannot have a right angle.

    Ⓑ A scalene triangle can also be an isosceles triangle.

    Ⓒ An equilateral triangle can only have one right angle.

    Ⓓ An equilateral triangle has three acute angles.

Use the hierarchy diagram to answer questions 4 and 5.

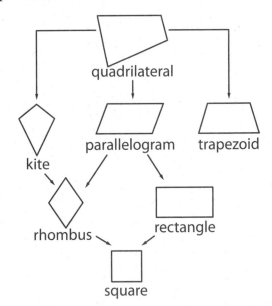

4. Rosendo cuts a quadrilateral from a piece of paper. He identifies one pair of parallel sides and at least two 60° angles in his polygon. Which of these **cannot** be a name for Rosendo's quadrilateral?

    Ⓐ trapezoid

    Ⓒ rhombus

    Ⓑ parallelogram

    Ⓓ rectangle

5. Rosendo read that a kite is a quadrilateral that has two pairs of adjacent congruent sides. He drew a special kite that had two pairs of parallel sides, four congruent sides, and four 90° angles. What other labels correctly name Rosendo's polygon?

    Ⓐ square only

    Ⓑ rhombus only

    Ⓒ rhombus and square

    Ⓓ trapezoid, rhombus, and square

Level 5

Use the Venn diagram to answer questions 1 and 2.

Ashley correctly draws this Venn diagram to show the relationships between quadrilaterals, parallelograms, rectangles, and squares.

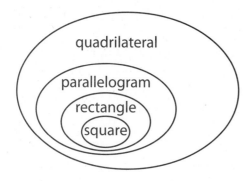

1. Ashley knows that every rectangle has two pairs of parallel sides. According to the diagram, which of these statements must also be true?

   Ⓐ Every quadrilateral has two pairs of parallel sides.

   Ⓑ Every square has two pairs of parallel sides.

   Ⓒ Every parallelogram has all of the attributes of a square.

   Ⓓ A parallelogram can never have 4 congruent sides.

2. Based on Ashley's Venn diagram, which of the following statements is **not** true?

   Ⓐ A square is a special type of rectangle.

   Ⓑ A rectangle is a special type of parallelogram.

   Ⓒ A parallelogram is a special type of quadrilateral.

   Ⓓ A quadrilateral is a special type of rectangle.

Use the diagram to answer questions 3 and 4.

Kelvin created this hierarchy to classify triangles according to their attributes.

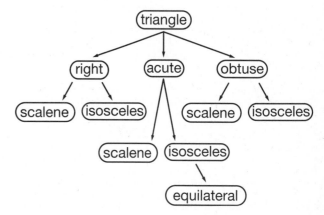

3. Which of the following is **not** a true statement?

   Ⓐ An acute triangle can also be an isosceles triangle.

   Ⓑ A right triangle can also be an equilateral triangle.

   Ⓒ An obtuse triangle can also be a scalene triangle.

   Ⓓ An isosceles triangle can also be a right triangle.

4. Kelvin finds a tile shaped like a triangle. He uses a ruler and protractor to discover that all sides are congruent and all angles are congruent. Kelvin writes the correct name of the triangle. What name does he write?

   Ⓐ right equilateral

   Ⓑ acute scalene

   Ⓒ equilateral

   Ⓓ obtuse isosceles

assessment

Use the diagram to answer questions 1 and 2.

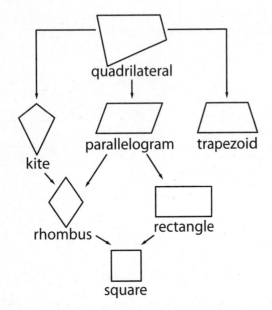

1. Which of the following figures can **always** be classified as a parallelogram?

   Ⓐ quadrilateral   Ⓒ trapezoid

   Ⓑ kite   Ⓓ square

2. Which of the following terms **cannot** be used to describe a rhombus?

   Ⓐ parallelogram   Ⓒ kite

   Ⓑ rectangle   Ⓓ quadrilateral

3. Brett wants to use these facts to create a hierarchy diagram.

   • An equilateral triangle has 3 congruent sides.

   • An isosceles triangle has 2 congruent sides.

   • A scalene triangle has no congruent sides.

   He creates four rough drafts. Which of Brett's rough drafts **best** organizes the triangles by their properties?

   Ⓐ
   equilateral
   ↓
   isosceles
   ↓
   scalene

   Ⓑ
   scalene
   ↓
   isosceles
   ↓
   equilateral

   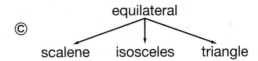

   Ⓒ

   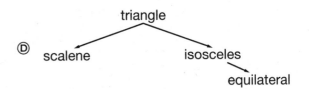

   Ⓓ

4. Mrs. Grimes asked her students to draw a hierarchy diagram for triangles. The diagrams drawn by Frankie and Kelly are shown.

   Mrs. Grimes said that both students have a correct start. Explain why their diagrams are different, yet both are correct.

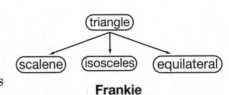

Frankie

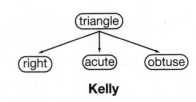

Kelly

_____

_____

Synthesis/Create

Create a Venn diagram showing the relationship between the following geometric figures: parallelogram, polygon, quadrilateral, rectangle, rhombus, square, trapezoid.

Journal: Analysis/Analyze

How is a hierarchy diagram for quadrilaterals like a family tree? How is it different?

_____

_____

_____

Something's Missing

Play *Something's Missing* with a partner. Each player needs a pencil and the game board below. Each pair of players needs 2 number cubes. In turn, each player chooses to roll 1 or 2 cubes and completes the missing part of the hierarchy with the number that matches the roll. For example, a player who rolls a five using one cube would complete the definition in the triangle chart. If a player rolls a number for a space that has already been completed, the player loses that turn, and play passes to the next player. The winner is the first person to correctly complete all missing parts in the hierarchy.

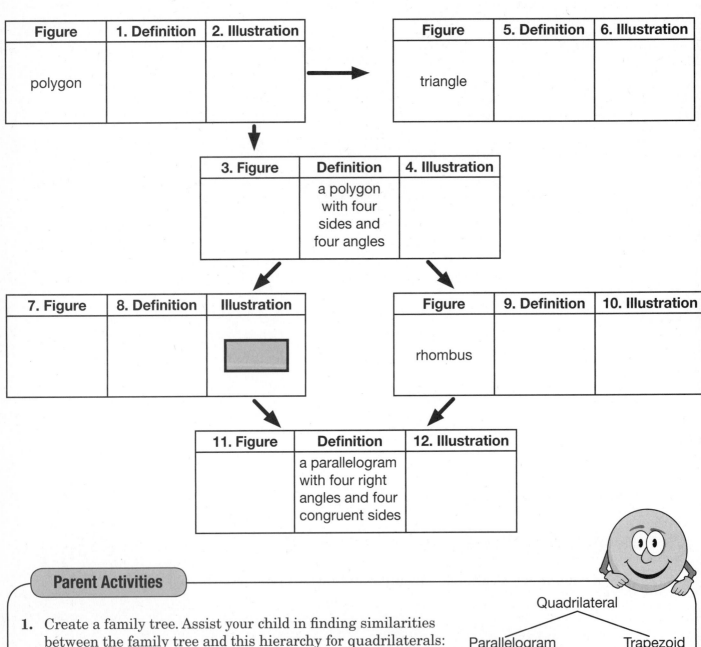

Figure	1. Definition	2. Illustration
polygon		

Figure	5. Definition	6. Illustration
triangle		

3. Figure	Definition	4. Illustration
	a polygon with four sides and four angles	

7. Figure	8. Definition	Illustration
		▭

Figure	9. Definition	10. Illustration
rhombus		

11. Figure	Definition	12. Illustration
	a parallelogram with four right angles and four congruent sides	

Parent Activities

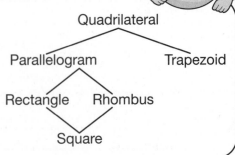

1. Create a family tree. Assist your child in finding similarities between the family tree and this hierarchy for quadrilaterals:

2. Using the diagram in the previous activity, help your child find all the "descendants" of a parallelogram (e.g., rectangle, rhombus, and square). Look for relationships among other figures as well.

Quadrilateral
Parallelogram   Trapezoid
Rectangle   Rhombus
Square

Notes

CHART YOUR SUCCESS

Color Mike or Molly *green* if your answer was correct, or *red* if your answer was incorrect.

	Question 1	Question 2	Question 3	Question 4	Question 5	Question 6	Question 7	Question 8	Total Right	Total Possible
Page 10 (5.OA.1) Grouping Symbols	☺	☺	☺	☺						/4
Page 16 (5.OA.2) Write Expressions	☺	☺	☺	☺	☺					/5
Page 22 (5.OA.3) Analyze Patterns	☺	☺	☺	☺	☺					/5
Page 28 (5.NBT.1) Place Value	☺	☺	☺	☺	☺					/5
Page 34 (5.NBT.2) Powers of Ten	☺	☺	☺	☺	☺	☺				/6
Page 40 (5.NBT.3) Compare Decimals	☺	☺	☺	☺	☺					/5
Page 46 (5.NBT.4) Round Decimals	☺	☺	☺	☺	☺					/5
Page 52 (5.NBT.5) Whole Numbers: ×	☺	☺	☺	☺	☺					/5
Page 58 (5.NBT.6) Whole Numbers: ÷	☺	☺	☺	☺	☺	☺				/6
Page 64 (5.NBT.7) Decimals: +, −, ×, ÷	☺	☺	☺	☺	☺					/5
Page 70 (5.NF.1) Fractions: +, −	☺	☺	☺	☺	☺					/5
Page 76 (5.NF.2) Fraction Word Problems: +, −	☺	☺	☺	☺	☺					/5
Page 82 (5.NF.3) Fractions as Division	☺	☺	☺	☺	☺	☺				/6

     Level 5

CHART YOUR SUCCESS

Color Mike or Molly **green** if your answer was correct, or **red** if your answer was incorrect.

	Question 1	Question 2	Question 3	Question 4	Question 5	Question 6	Question 7	Total Right	Total Possible
Page 88 (5.NF.4) Fractions × Whole Numbers	😊	😊	😊	😊	😊				/5
Page 94 (5.NF.5) Multiplication as Scaling	😊	😊	😊	😊	😊				/5
Page 100 (5.NF.6) Fraction Word Problems: ×	😊	😊	😊	😊	😊				/5
Page 106 (5.NF.7) Fractions and Whole Numbers: ÷	😊	😊	😊	😊	😊				/5
Page 112 (5.MD.1) Convert Measurements	😊	😊	😊	😊	😊	😊			/6
Page 118 (5.MD.2) Line Plots	😊	😊	😊	😊	😊				/5
Page 124 (5.MD.3/5.MD.4) Volume	😊	😊	😊	😊	😊				/5
Page 130 (5.MD.5) Volume: ×/+	😊	😊	😊	😊	😊				/5
Page 136 (5.G.1) Ordered Pairs	😊	😊	😊	😊	😊				/5
Page 142 (5.G.2) Coordinate Plane	😊	😊	😊	😊	😊				/5
Page 148 (5.G.3) Attributes of 2-D Figures	😊	😊	😊	😊	😊				/5
Page 154 (5.G.4) Classify 2-D Figures	😊	😊	😊	😊					/4

Level 5

Notes

MATH GLOSSARY

A

acute angle – an angle measuring less than 90°

acute triangle – a triangle with three acute angles

addends – numbers that are added

adjacent – side-by-side, adjoining

angle – the figure made by 2 rays that extend from a common endpoint

approximate – *verb*: to estimate; to come close to; *adjective*: almost exact or correct

area – the number of square units needed to cover a surface

area of base – in a three-dimensional figure, the area, in square units, of the base of the figure

attribute – a characteristic or property of a shape or thing

axis/axes – the horizontal (*x*-axis) and vertical (*y*-axis) number lines on a coordinate plane

B

braces – symbols used to group part of a mathematical expression or equation: { }

brackets – symbols used to group part of a mathematical expression or equation: [ ]

C

capacity – a measure of the amount of liquid a container will hold

centimeter (cm) – a metric unit used to measure length

circle – a two-dimensional figure consisting of a closed curve with all points the same distance from the center

common denominator – a denominator that is the same in 2 or more fractions

compare – to determine whether two or more numbers or quantities are greater than, less than, or equal to one another

compose – joining numbers to create tens, hundreds, thousands, etc.; joining or putting together parts to create a whole

congruent – having the same size and shape

coordinate plane – a plane formed by 2 perpendicular number lines called axes; every point can be named by an ordered pair of numbers

coordinates – an ordered pair of numbers (*x*, *y*) used to locate a point on a coordinate plane

corresponding terms – two numbers or elements that occupy the same position in two different patterns

cubic centimeter (cm^3) – a unit, shaped like a cube with dimensions of 1 cm x 1 cm x 1 cm, used to measure volume

cubic foot (ft^3) – a unit, shaped like a cube with dimensions of 1 ft x 1 ft x 1 ft, used to measure volume

cubic inch (in^3) – a unit, shaped like a cube with dimensions of 1 in x 1 in x 1 in, used to measure volume

cubic meter (m^3) – a unit, shaped like a cube with dimensions of 1 m x 1 m x 1 m, used to measure volume

cubic unit – a unit, shaped like a cube with dimensions of 1 unit x 1 unit x 1 unit, used to measure volume

cubic yard (yd) – a unit, shaped like a cube with dimensions of 1 yd x 1 yd x 1 yd, used to measure volume

cup – a customary unit for measuring capacity

customary system of measurement – the measurement system used most often in the United States

D

data – a collection of facts or information gathered by observation, questioning, or measuring, usually displayed in a chart, table, or graph

decimal number – a number that uses a decimal point to show tenths, hundredths, and thousandths

decimal point – the dot used to separate the ones place from the tenths place in a decimal number

decompose – to break down or break apart into smaller parts

denominator – the bottom number in a fraction; the total number of equal parts

difference – the answer to a subtraction problem

digit – the symbols 0, 1, 2, 3, 4, 5, 6, 7, 8, and 9 used to write numbers

dimension – measurement of a geometric shape in one direction

dividend – the number to be divided in a division problem

division – the operation of making equal groups to find the number in each group or to find the number of equal groups

divisor – the number by which another number is divided

double – twice as much

E

edge – the line segment where two faces of a solid figure meet

equal (=) – having the same value

equation – a number sentence that uses the equals sign to show that two expressions are equal

equilateral triangle – a triangle with three congruent sides

equivalent – the same in value or amount

equivalent fractions – two or more fractions that are equal

estimate – *noun*: an answer that is close to the exact answer; *verb*: to guess about

evaluate – to find the value of an expression

expanded form – a way to write numbers that shows the value of each digit

exponent – the number of times the base is to be multiplied by itself

expression – a mathematical combination of numbers, operations, and/or variables

F

factor – a number that is multiplied by another number to find a product

foot (ft) – a customary unit used to measure length

fraction – a number that names a part of a whole or part of a group

G

gallon (gal) – a customary unit used to measure capacity

gram (g) – a metric unit used to measure mass

greater than (>) and **less than** (<) – the symbols used to compare two numbers

grouping symbols – braces, brackets, or parentheses used to group numbers, symbols, and/or variables; calculations within grouping symbols must be completed first

H

height – the distance from bottom to top

hierarchy – an arrangement or grouping that shows how items in one category relate to items in another category

horizontal – the direction from left to right; parallel to the horizon

hour (hr) – a unit used to measure time

hundredth – one of 100 equal parts; the second place to the right of the decimal point

I

improper fraction – a fraction whose numerator is greater than or equal to its denominator

inch (in) – a customary unit used to measure length

isosceles triangle – a triangle with two congruent sides

K

kilogram (kg) – a metric unit used to measure mass

kilometer (km) – a metric unit used to measure length

kite – a quadrilateral with two pairs of congruent, adjacent sides

L

least common denominator (LCD) – the least common multiple of the denominators of every fraction in a given set of fractions

length – the distance from one end of an object to the other

line plot – a graph using marks above a number on a number line to show the frequency of data

liquid volume – the amount or quantity of liquid in a container; capacity

liter (L) – a metric unit used to measure liquid volume

lowest terms – the simplest form of a fraction in which the numerator and denominator have no common factors except 1

M

mass – the measure of the amount of matter in an object; gravity does not affect mass

measure – to find the size, weight/mass, or capacity of an item using a given unit

meter (m) – a metric unit used to measure length

metric system of measurement – a measurement system used throughout the world, based on multiples of 10

mile (mi) – a customary unit used to measure length or distance

milligram (mg) – a metric unit used to measure mass

milliliter (mL) – a metric unit used to measure capacity

minute (min) – a unit used to measure time

mixed number – a number made up of a whole number and a fraction, such as $2\frac{3}{4}$, $5\frac{1}{8}$, etc.

multiple – the product of a given number and any whole number

multiplication – the operation using repeated addition of the same number; combining equal groups

multiply – to join or combine equal groups

N

number line – a line on which points correspond to numbers

number sentence – a mathematical sentence that uses numbers and symbols

numerator – the top number in a fraction; how many equal parts are being considered

numerical expression – a mathematical combination of numbers, operations, and/or variables

O

obtuse angle – an angle measuring more than 90° but less than 180°

obtuse triangle – a triangle that has one angle greater than 90°

ordered pair – a pair of numbers used to locate a point on a coordinate plane

origin – the point on the coordinate plane where the *x*-axis and the *y*-axis intersect; (0, 0)

ounce (oz) – a customary unit used to measure weight

P

parallel – never meeting or intersecting; always the same distance apart

parallel lines – two lines in the same plane that never intersect

parallelogram – a quadrilateral with opposite sides that are parallel and congruent

parentheses – symbols used to group part of a mathematical expression or equation; ( )

partial product – when multiplying by a multi-digit multiplier, the result obtained when a number is multiplied by one of the digits

perpendicular – intersecting at right angles

perpendicular lines – lines that intersect at one point and form right angles

pint (pt) – a customary unit used to measure capacity

place value – the value determined by the position of a digit in a number

plot – to determine and mark points on a coordinate plane

point – an exact location or position; a point may be represented by a dot

polygon – a closed figure made of line segments

pound (lb) – a customary unit used to measure weight

power – the number of times the base is to be multiplied by itself; exponent

power of ten – the value of ten multiplied by itself the number of times shown by the exponent; $10^3 = 10 \times 10 \times 10 = 1000$

product – the answer to a multiplication problem

proper fraction – a fraction in which the numerator is smaller than the denominator (e.g., $\frac{2}{5}, \frac{5}{8}, \frac{7}{10}$)

Q

quadrilateral – a polygon with 4 sides and 4 angles

quart (qt) – a customary unit used to measure capacity

quotient – the answer to a division problem

R

reasonable – logical or sensible

rectangle – a parallelogram with four right angles

rectangular prism – a 3-dimensional figure with 6 rectangular faces

regular polygon – a polygon in which all sides are the same length and all angles have the same measure

remainder – the number left over after dividing into equal groups

rhombus – a parallelogram whose four sides are congruent and whose opposite angles are congruent

right angle – an angle with a measure of 90°

right triangle – a triangle with one right angle

round – to approximate a number to a given place value

rule – a procedure that a pattern must follow

S

scalene triangle – a triangle with no congruent sides

second (s) – a unit used to measure small amounts of time

sequence – an ordered set of numbers or shapes arranged according to a rule or pattern

simplify – to write a fraction in lowest terms

square – a special rectangle with 4 sides of equal measure

sum – the answer to an addition problem

T

tenth – one of 10 equal parts; the first place to the right of the decimal point

term (of a sequence) – one of the numbers in a sequence or pattern

thousandth – one of 1000 equal parts; the third place to the right of the decimal point

trapezoid – a quadrilateral with exactly one pair of parallel sides

triangle – a polygon with 3 sides and 3 angles

triple – three times as much

two-dimensional figure – a plane figure that has length and width

U

unit cube – a cube in which each dimension (length, width, and height) measures 1 unit

unit fraction – a fraction with a numerator of 1, such as $\frac{1}{2}, \frac{1}{4}, \frac{1}{8}$, etc.

V

vertical – straight up and down; perpendicular to the horizon

volume – the number of cubic units needed to fill the space occupied by a solid

W

whole numbers – the set of counting numbers and zero: 0, 1, 2, 3, 4, ...

width – the measure or distance across something from one side to the other

X

x-axis – the horizontal axis on the coordinate plane

x-coordinate – the first number in an ordered pair, locating a point on the x-axis of a coordinate plane

Y

yard (yd) – a customary unit for measuring length or distance

y-axis – the vertical axis on the coordinate plane

y-coordinate – the second number in an ordered pair, locating a point on the y-axis of a coordinate plane

Notes

GRADE 5
Mathematics Chart

TIME

365 days = 1 year

12 months = 1 year

52 weeks = 1 year

7 days = 1 week

24 hours = 1 day

60 minutes = 1 hour

60 seconds = 1 minute

LENGTH

Customary	Metric
5280 feet = 1 mile	1000 meters = 1 kilometer
1760 yards = 1 mile	100 centimeters = 1 meter
36 inches = 1 yard	1000 millimeters = 1 meter
3 feet = 1 yard	10 millimeters = 1 centimeter
12 inches = 1 foot	

Inches

0

1

2

3

4

5

6

GRADE 5
Mathematics Chart

LIQUID VOLUME (Capacity)

Customary	Metric
4 quarts = 1 gallon	1000 milliliters = 1 liter
2 pints = 1 quart	
2 cups = 1 pint	

MASS

Customary	Metric
2000 pounds = 1 ton	1000 grams = 1 kilogram
16 ounces = 1 pound	

FORMULAS

Perimeter of a rectangle

$P = 2 \times (l + w)$

Area of a rectangle

$A = l \times w$

Volume of a rectangular prism

$V = l \times w \times h$

Centimeters

Level 5

Notes

Notes

Notes

Notes

 Level 5

Notes

Notes

Level 5

Notes